AN INTRODUCTION TO
CRAFT DESIGN AND TECHNOLOGY

STEWART DUNN

Unwin Hyman

Published by
UNWIN HYMAN LIMITED
15-17 Broadwick Street
London W1V 1FP

© Stewart Dunn 1986
First published by Bell & Hyman 1986
Reprinted 1987 (twice), 1988

British Library Cataloguing in Publication Data

Dunn, Stewart
   An introduction to craft, design and technology
   1. Manual training—England 2. Design
   —Study and teaching (Secondary)—
   England 3. Technology—Study and
   Teaching—England
   I. Title
   607'.42   T107

   ISBN 0-7135-2651-3

Designed by Snap Graphics
Illustrated by RDL Artset Ltd.
Cover illustration by Iain Lanyon

Typeset by Cambridge Photosetting Services
Printed and bound in Hong Kong
by Colorcraft Limited

CONTENTS

Preface

Craft, Design and Technology has changed over the years from a materials based subject such as Woodwork and Metalwork to a subject that now centres around the **design process** with its problem solving approach. The products designed should be made with the best materials and technology that are available, including the use of plastics, construction kits, computers etc.

This book has been written so that pupils can be given a good introduction into CDT before starting specialist examination courses. It is therefore aimed mainly at the 11–14/15-year-olds, but is suitable for anybody who is being introduced to:

1 The *Design* process (or **Problem solving**),
2 *Craft* skills in wood, metal or plastics,
3 the *Technologies* of: **materials, structures, mechanisms, control with computers, electrics and electronics, and energy.**

The tabbed sections, index and cross references given within the text make this book easy to use. It has over 100 project ideas illustrated and is invaluable as an ideas book. Exercises are given throughout the book. A practical mechanisms course using kits, and a practical electrics and electronics course, are also included. Both simple and more advanced project ideas and concepts are covered, providing something suitable for all abilities and ages.

It is sometimes said that pupils find it hard to apply the design process and that they lack interest. Hopefully this book can help overcome these problems, especially if work of the type described in this book is taught before the examinations options are started.

I hope you will find this book interesting and enjoyable.

S. Dunn

The author has taught and examined the main subject areas of Craft, Design and Technology to examination level, such as Design and Craft, Technology and Graphical Communication. He has also been on advisory panels, helped develop and test new teaching materials and helped run in-service courses for teachers on various CDT topics.

Acknowledgements

I would like to thank all those who have helped in any way with the production of this book. Thanks go in particular to my wife for much of the word processing and other help given; to Mark Dunn, Mr S. Green and Jan Shimmin for the many hours spent checking the text and illustrations; the headmaster, and pupils of Hollinswood Middle School who have tried and tested many of the project ideas. I would also like to acknowledge the following firms who have kindly provided photographs and practical help:

LEGO® UK Limited, for practical help and advice, and photographs on pages 26, 28, 78, 79, 81, 82, 83, 101.
Artur Fischer (UK) Limited, for Fischertechnik robot photograph on page 78.
Candy Appliances Limited, for dishwasher photograph on page 21.
GEC (Radio and Television) Limited, for telephone photograph on page 21.
Big Box Limited (Artstraws), for practical help.
Mr D. Roberts, for sailing photograph on page 71.
Barnaby's Picture Library, for Humber Bridge photograph on page 71.
Royal Aeronautical Society, for Gossamer Condor photograph on page 71.
Associated Press, for the track racing bicycle photograph on page 73.
Pilot One, for the photograph of a computer controlled interface and crane on page 102.

SAFETY IN THE WORKSHOP

Safety must be considered at all times in the workshop. If you are considerate to others, tidy and prepared to 'ask if unsure', you should be a reasonably safe person. But remember that an eye or an arm cannot be replaced.

Safety rules

1 GENERAL

- **Ask if unsure.**
- Wear apron, goggles, strong shoes and any other safety clothing that may be needed. If you have long hair it will need to be tied up.
- Ties and other loose clothing must either be removed or tucked in.
- Do **not** fool about in the workshop.
- Do **not** rush about.
- Do **not** interfere with other people's work.
- Tidy tools away after use.
- Extra special care needs to be taken with your eyes — protect them with goggles.
- Report any breakages or injuries at once.
- Stop buttons are for use in emergency only.
- Sharp edges must be treated with respect (e.g. newly cut materials, chisels, etc.).
- Hold your work firmly when cutting, drilling, etc.
- Paints and resins can cause an awful mess. Plan ahead and work on a sheet of polythene or newspaper in a well ventilated place.
- Acid needs special care — ask your teacher about this.
- Use a face mask if the work creates dust.
- Good ventilation is required if painting, working with plastic resins or casting.

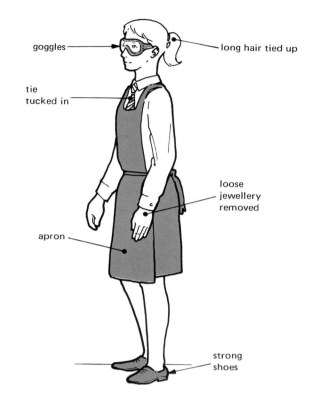

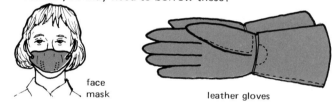

Sometimes you may need to borrow these:

face mask

leather gloves

2 FIRST AID

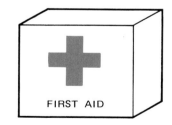

FIRST AID

All injuries **MUST** be reported to the teacher who will decide what has to be done. **Do you know where the first aid box is?** Below are a few first aid measures you should be aware of.

Burns – Place in cold running water for at least 10 minutes.

Bad Bleeding – Try to raise the cut above heart level to reduce bleeding (e.g. lay on floor and lift a bleeding leg up).

Eye – If a speck of dust gets into your eye, try to wash it out with an 'eye glass'.

Fainting – Lay the patient down to increase blood flow to the head (lift legs a little).

WHAT'S WRONG HERE?

PAINT

GLUE

SAFETY WITH MACHINES

Machines can be very dangerous: NEVER use a machine unless you have been instructed in its safe use. Some machines are too dangerous for pupils to use and can **ONLY** be operated by **teachers** (e.g. the circular saw).

GENERAL POINTS RELATING TO MOST MACHINES
- Only one person per machine.
- Safety guards and goggles to be used.
- Double check before starting.
- Tidy up after use.

DRILLING MACHINE
- **Hold** the work **firmly.**
- **Tighten** the drill, ensuring it is central.
- Remove the 'chuck key' from the chuck.
- Use **guard** and **goggles.**

Note **Centre punch** metal before drilling. Support **thin materials** with a piece of scrap wood. **Withdraw** the 'drill bit' occasionally to remove swarf if drilling a deep hole.

SPEED OF DRILL
The **speed** the 'bit' in a drill turns needs to be considered carefully. Your teacher will probably have selected a speed for you but you should be aware of the following:

Large drill bits need slow speeds.
Small drill bits need faster speeds.

Pillar drill

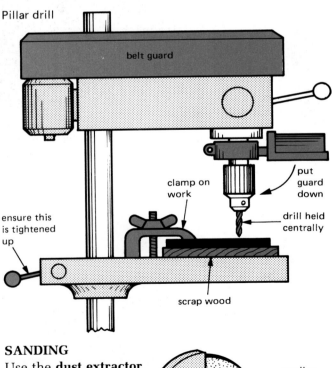

belt guard

ensure this is tightened up

clamp on work

put guard down

drill held centrally

scrap wood

SANDING
Use the **dust extractor.**

Sanding disc
Use goggles, guard and turn on dust extractor.

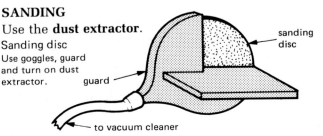

sanding disc

guard

to vacuum cleaner

BRAZING HEARTH
Plan ahead to avoid too much movement with hot materials.

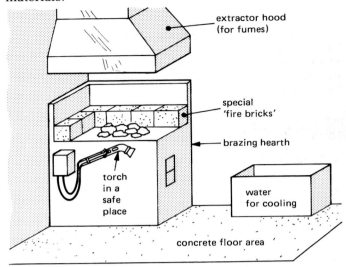

extractor hood (for fumes)

special 'fire bricks'

brazing hearth

torch in a safe place

water for cooling

concrete floor area

SOLDERING IRON
Avoid melting the mains wire, inhaling the fumes and burning yourself accidentally.

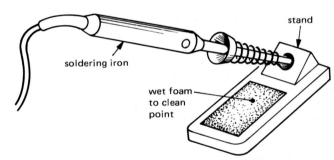

soldering iron

stand

wet foam to clean point

WHAT'S WRONG HERE? (8 THINGS)

drilling machine

FAST
V. FAST
SLOW
SPEED

GENERAL INTRODUCTION

This book will give you a good introduction into CRAFT, DESIGN AND TECHNOLOGY. It has been written so there is something for everybody of all abilities and interests. The material has been designed to be versatile.

It can be used —

- to show that CDT is an interesting and exciting subject.
- as the main class text and reference book for CDT.
- for its many design briefs and ideas to help you get started.
- with **homework** (there are set exercises and problems given).
- with **solving problems** (using the text and ideas provided).
- as an **ideas book** (over 100 ideas are given).
- to show how easy-to-make vehicles can be built and tested.
- to help with construction kit building (photographs of kits solving problems etc.).
- as a revision book.
- to prepare for tests.
- to help select the best materials.
- to provide guidance when designing.
- to show how industry uses the design process.
- to help with aesthetic considerations.
- to help consider ergonomic factors.
- for practical courses in:
  - A Structures
  - B Mechanisms
  - C Electrics and Electronics
- for a basic graphical communication course.
- for help with graphical presentation.
- for modelling ideas and techniques.
- to provide ideas for shapes (pages 30 and 31).
- to help with mixing colours (colour circle on page 33 and back cover).
- to help with drawing and sketching techniques.
- to help with **woodwork** (tools and equipment used etc.).
- to help with **metalwork** (tools and equipment used etc.).
- to help with **plastics work** (tools and equipment used etc.).

How can you find what you want?

You can use either —
— the **rear cover index** together with the **tabs** on the pages for chapter headings.
— the **Contents page**.
— the **index at the back** for specific headings.

Now see if you can find the following as quickly as possible using the method you think best:
  (a) The page about bridges.
  (b) How to enamel.
  (c) Ergonomics (human factors).

A marble jump made from 12 Artstraws, adhesive tape and two strips of card, the aim being to make the marble jump as far as possible.

A plastic vacuum formed racing car made by a 12-year-old pupil. The wheels were made with the help of a hole saw.

THE DESIGN PROCESS

The design process has a very important place in Craft, Design and Technology and as such is explained in some detail in this book. It is sometimes called 'product design'.

To design successfully we need to take into account many factors such as: sizes, cost, materials, appearance, construction, safety, various ideas etc.

Diagram A opposite shows the design process stages drawn in a circular shape to illustrate that the design process should be flexible and stages can be repeated, if needed, until a good product finally emerges. For example, the design of a car goes through the design process several times before the public sees it.

Diagram B below shows the same design process in a fixed order, i.e. a straight line. This is the method used in this book because it is easier for the beginner to understand. The arrows indicate that it is not really a rigid process, as explained above.

The next page explains the design process in more detail.

Page 6 shows an example of 'The design process in practice'.

Page 7 shows 'The design process as used in industry'.

Note The headings used in this book have been selected because they are easy to remember; different headings are sometimes used by other people.

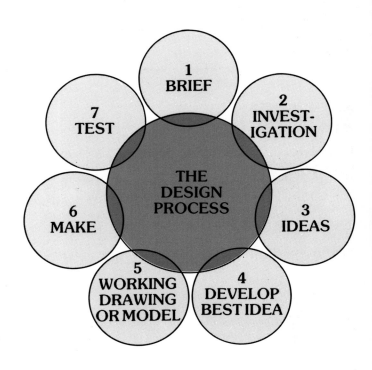

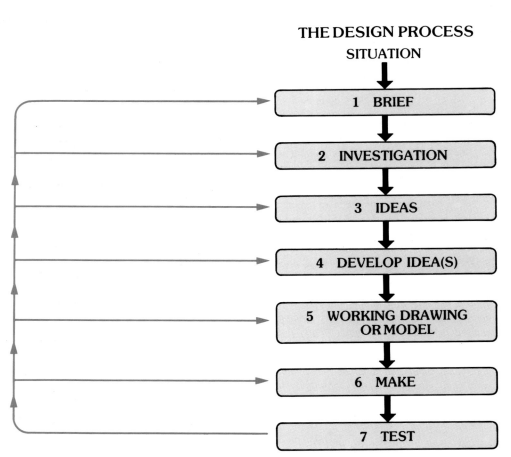

THE DESIGN PROCESS — A SUMMARY

1

BRIEF (or PROBLEM)
The **brief** is a short statement indicating what you intend to design and make.
Note. A detailed design brief also states any restrictions placed on the design such as: materials, sizes, cost, time allowed, processes to be used.

2

INVESTIGATION
The **investigation** stage is carried out by thinking and researching the problems involved. One of the best ways of doing this is to carry out the following steps:
- **Functions** (requirements)   List the main functions the design must achieve if it is to be successful.
- **Questions and comments**   Jot down any you have on things like: **appearance, sizes, human factors, strength, materials, cost, construction, fittings needed, safety** etc.
- **Research**   Carry out any research that is necessary. This includes: looking at books and magazines, questioning other people (including your teacher), visiting shops to obtain ideas, prices, materials available etc.

Note. Include sketches, magazine cuttings etc. where it will help.

3

IDEAS
Various **ideas** and possible solutions — are considered in sketch form (or in model form) together with explanatory notes where needed.
Note. This stage should stretch your imagination; even so-called silly ideas should be included, as they may prove to be the germ of a great idea.

4

DEVELOP IDEA(S)
The most feasible ideas and solutions are considered in more detail, they can be completely new ideas or new versions of old ideas. The main things you need to decide on are:
- the materials you hope to use,
- the main dimensions,
- possible joints and construction methods,
- possible surface finishes,
- how the parts can be made.

5

WORKING DRAWING OR MODEL
The **working drawing or working model** should provide enough information to enable someone else to make your best idea.
Note. It often saves time later if you 'plan ahead on paper how you will make it', indicating what machines are to be used and at what stage.

6

MAKE
The product is now made with improvements to your design if needed.
Note. You may need to learn new skills before you can make it.

7

TEST
The product made is tested to see if it does its job successfully. If not, you may need to make some small alterations or even start again!

For a more detailed description of the **design process** see pages 19–28.

THE DESIGN PROCESS IN PRACTICE

CRAFT, DESIGN AND TECHN[...]

1 BRIEF

Design and make a FUN HOOK to hang
(e.g. tea towels, bath bag etc)
It must have some form of decoration

2 INVESTIGATION

FUNCTIONS
  It must look attractive.
  The hook must be strong.
  It must have no sharp edges.
QUESTIONS AND COMMENTS
  I will probably hang an apron or
  How will it be fixed to the wall?
  What materials are suitable?

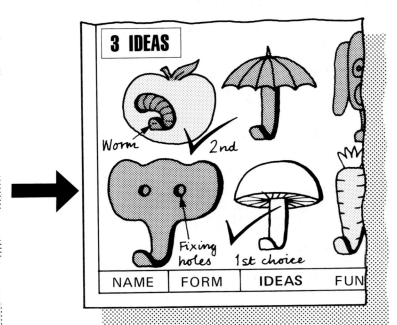

3 IDEAS

Worm
2nd
Fixing holes
1st choice

| NAME | FORM | IDEAS | FUN |

4 DEVELOP IDEA(S)

Screw
Double sided tape pad
To fit on a kitchen wall
Painted steel or acrylic

| NAME | FORM | DEVELOP IDEA(S) |

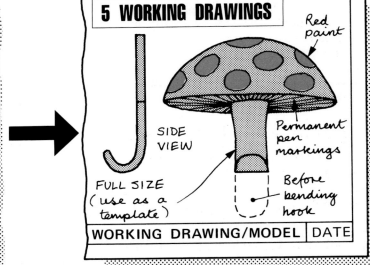

5 WORKING DRAWINGS

Red paint
SIDE VIEW
Permanent pen markings
FULL SIZE (use as a template)
Before bending hook

| WORKING DRAWING/MODEL | DATE |

6 MAKE

The fun hook being heated on a strip heater prior to the hook being bent.

7 TEST

Apron being tested on the hook

THE DESIGN PROCESS AS USED IN INDUSTRY

The production of a new car model is given as an example (it can take several years from the decision to produce a new car to the selling of the first car).

1 BRIEF

This is a short precise statement indicating what is to be designed and made. The directors and management of a firm usually decide this.

2 INVESTIGATION

Salesman, designers, market researchers directors and production managers investigate and research the problems associated with the design brief.

3 IDEAS

All sorts of ideas are considered and usually recorded as notes. Sketches and drawings.

4 DEVELOPMENT OF BEST IDEAS

The best ideas are developed in great detail.

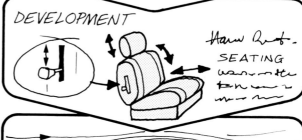

5 WORKING DRAWINGS AND MODELS

Working drawings and models are made and checked before prototypes can be made.

MODEL IN WIND TUNNEL

6 MAKE IT

Prototypes are made and examined as to their possible sales potential.

ASSEMBLY LINE

7 TESTS

Tests are made to ensure that the product is reliable, safe, and attractive to potential customers.

CRASH TESTING

THREE EXAMPLES OF THE DESIGN PROCESS

Three examples of the design process are given starting on this page and finishing on page 18.

EXAMPLE 1
This example shows how a keyfob was designed by a girl. The investigation stage is only partly shown due to lack of space (the next example shows a full investigation).

EXAMPLE 2
This example shows the process used to design a spinning executive toy. It shows the complete design process and illustrates the use of preprinted design sheets.

EXAMPLE 3
This example shows the design of a 'steady hand game' originally inspired by the buzz game sometimes seen at fund-raising events. It is a popular project that involves some basic electricity. The original 'design brief' was given by the teacher on the first design sheet. The working drawing was drawn to scale (half full size); this avoided the need to dimension all parts.

Example 1: A keyfob

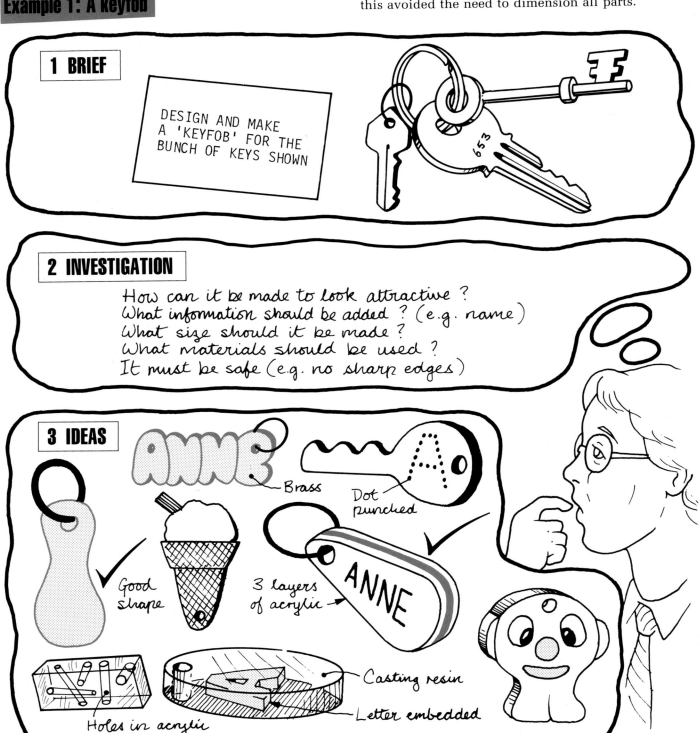

1 BRIEF

DESIGN AND MAKE A 'KEYFOB' FOR THE BUNCH OF KEYS SHOWN

653

2 INVESTIGATION

How can it be made to look attractive?
What information should be added? (e.g. name)
What size should it be made?
What materials should be used?
It must be safe (e.g. no sharp edges)

3 IDEAS

ANNE

Brass

Dot punched

Good shape

3 layers of acrylic

ANNE

Casting resin

Letter embedded

Holes in acrylic

4 DEVELOP IDEA(S)

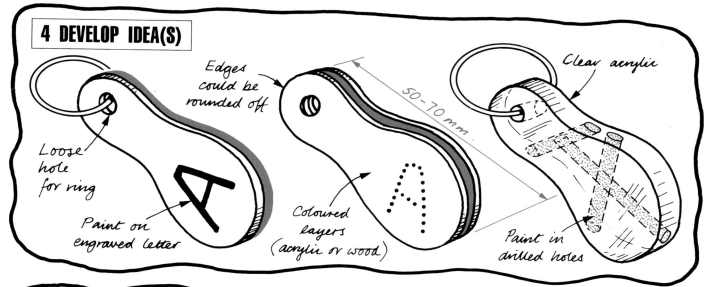

Loose hole for ring

Paint on engraved letter

Edges could be rounded off

Coloured layers (acrylic or wood)

50–70 mm

Clear acrylic

Paint in drilled holes

5 WORKING DRAWING

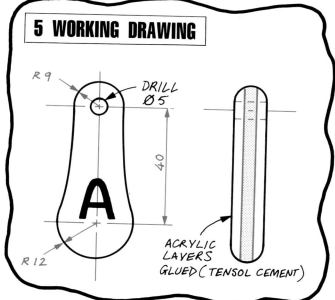

R 9

DRILL Ø 5

40

R 12

ACRYLIC LAYERS GLUED (TENSOL CEMENT)

6 MAKE

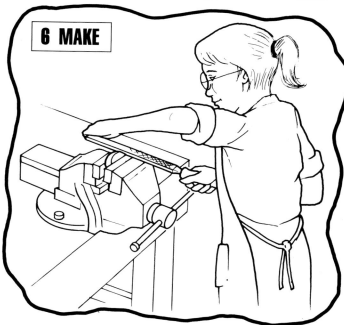

7 TESTS

IT LOOKS GOOD AND FEELS NICE. THE HOLE NEEDED TO BE COUNTERSUNK TO ALLOW THE RING TO MOVE EASILY.

The keyfob in use. It was given its final finish on a polishing machine.

Example 2: An executive toy

CRAFT, DESIGN AND TECHNOLOGY

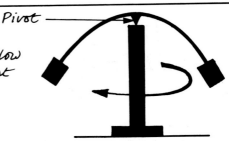

1 BRIEF

Design and make an 'executive toy' that pivots similar to the diagram shown opposite.

NOTE: weights below pivot point must be heavier than that above it.

2 INVESTIGATION

MAIN FUNCTIONS

1. Must be attractive.
2. To spin for quite a long time.
3. To be reasonably robust.

HOW CAN ARMS BE ARRANGED?

Equal weight and equal length

Long arm, small weight

Short arm + heavy weight

WHAT SLOWS THE ARMS DOWN?

Friction on the pivot and air resistance must be kept to a minimum.

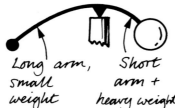

Good

Poor idea →

Too much wind resistance

Improved idea

Twisted round

ERGONOMIC FACTORS

It must be easy to turn by hand.

Finger holds

Tops should be easy to spin
Joints : must withstand knocks

Glued or brazed or a tight fit

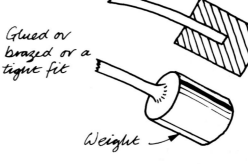

Weight →

Stronger if wire inside and glued or brazed

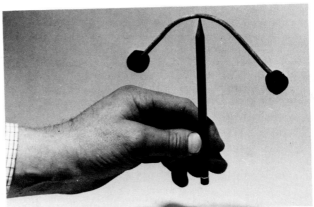

Wire and plasticine model: experimenting with arm shapes and weights to see how well it spins.

| JENNIFER OVING | 3S | EXECUTIVE TOY | DATE |

3 IDEAS

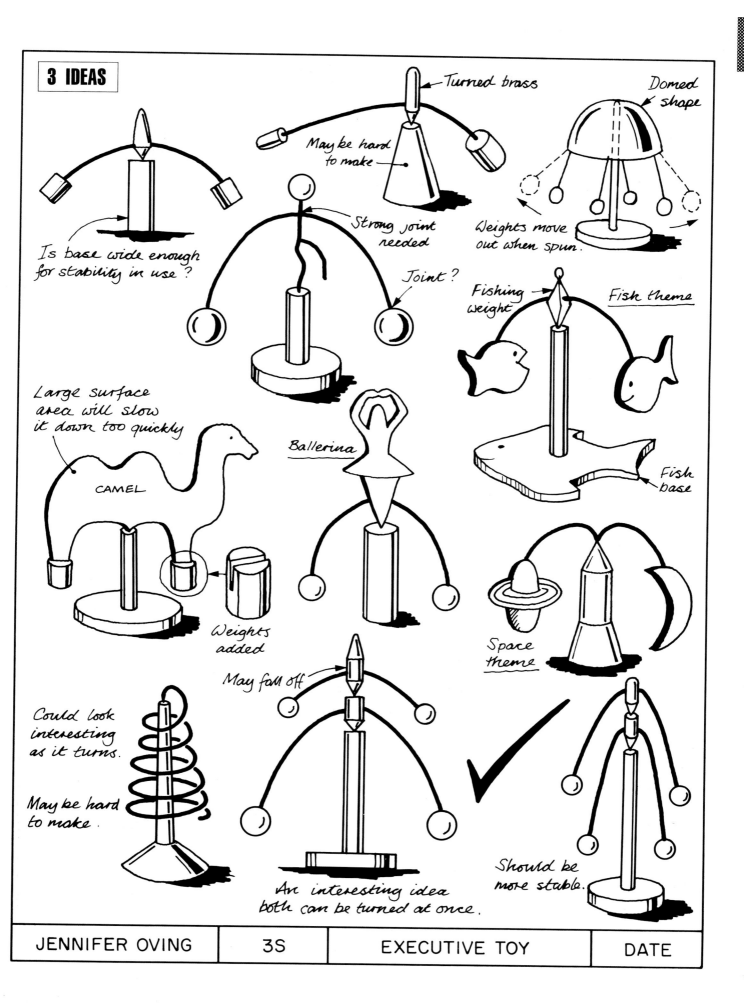

Turned brass

Domed shape

May be hard to make

Weights move out when spun.

Is base wide enough for stability in use?

Strong joint needed

Joint?

Fishing weight

Fish theme

Large surface area will slow it down too quickly

CAMEL

Ballerina

Fish base

Weights added

Space theme

Could look interesting as it turns.

May be hard to make.

May fall off

An interesting idea both can be turned at once.

Should be more stable.

| JENNIFER OVING | 3S | EXECUTIVE TOY | DATE |

Example 2: An executive toy (continued)

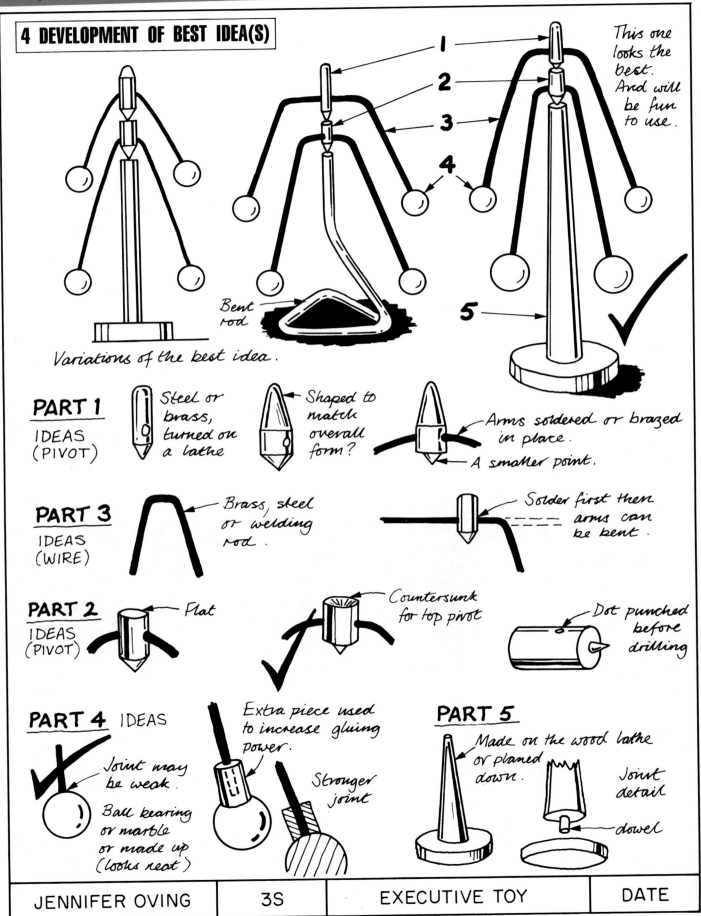

4 DEVELOPMENT OF BEST IDEA(S)

This one looks the best. And will be fun to use.

Bent rod

Variations of the best idea.

PART 1
IDEAS (PIVOT)

Steel or brass, turned on a lathe

Shaped to match overall form?

Arms soldered or brazed in place.

A smaller point.

PART 3
IDEAS (WIRE)

Brass, steel or welding rod.

Solder first then arms can be bent.

PART 2
IDEAS (PIVOT)

Flat

Countersunk for top pivot

Dot punched before drilling

PART 4 IDEAS

Joint may be weak.

Ball bearing or marble or made up (looks neat)

Extra piece used to increase gluing power.

Stronger joint

PART 5

Made on the wood lathe or planed down.

Joint detail

dowel

| JENNIFER OVING | 3S | EXECUTIVE TOY | DATE |

5 WORKING MODEL

A working model of the executive toy.

It took 20 minutes to make the model using plasticine, wooden dowel and some thin wire. The weakest joint was where the dowel and wire joined together. The model did not spin very well because the pivot was unsatisfactory. The final executive toy used metal pivots which spin well.

7 TESTS

Does it satisfy the functions listed at the Investigation stage?

Functions
Does it look attractive?
Yes. I believe it is quite attractive especially when in use.

To spin for a long time.
It spins for about two minutes but it depends on how hard it is twisted.

To be robust
The model was very weak but the final version has withstood a few falls so far.

Other comments
A better harder sharper point would improve the spin time. The hardest part was fixing the ball bearings on.

| R OVING | 3 S | EXECUTIVE TOY | DATE |

6 MAKE

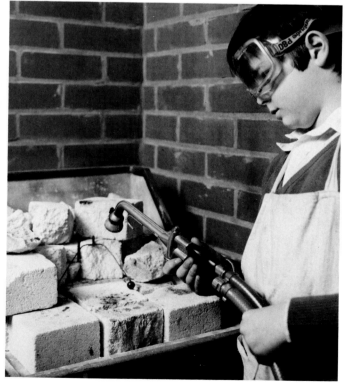

The metal pivot being brazed to the steel arms, the fire bricks are placed as shown so that the joint is heated as quickly as possible.

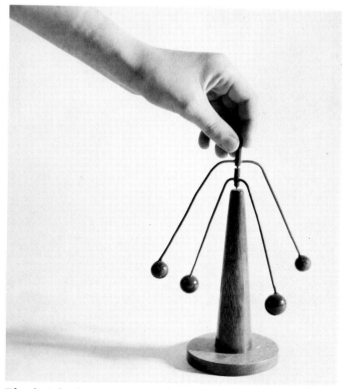

The finished executive toy being tested to see how long it will spin for.

Example 3: A steady hand game

CRAFT, DESIGN AND TECHNOLOGY

1 BRIEF

Design and make a STEADY HAND GAME in the school workshop.
First experiment with the electric kit provided to get a feel for the kind of circuits that are possible. Start by making a similar circuit to that drawn opposite.

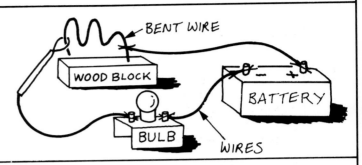

2 INVESTIGATION

List of functions
a. Must be fun to use
b. To look good
c. To be easy to use (ergonomics)

What electric parts can be obtained?
Indicators — bell, buzzer, bulb, L.E.D.
            connected to a computer etc.

Samples from catalogues

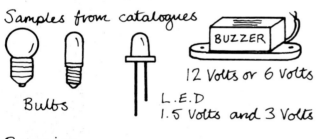

Bulbs

BUZZER
12 Volts or 6 Volts
L.E.D
1.5 Volts and 3 Volts

Batteries

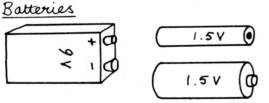

1.5V

1.5V

Also calculator and watch batteries could be used (low current)

Switches Not really needed if probe is not touching bent wire shape

The simplest circuit.

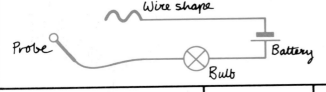

Wire shape
Probe
Bulb
Battery

What determines the size?
The handle of the probe and the whole game must be comfortable to use.

Comfortable in the hand

Container large enough to hold battery & buzzer or bulb

Cost
The cheapest version would be to use a bulb and borrow a battery (when required) from something else (e.g. a torch)

This would mean that the battery must be easy to remove.

Materials
The container would be best if it does not conduct electricity.
The bent wire frame must be a good conductor
e.g. steel — rusts ✗
      brass rod — brazing rod ✓
      aluminium ✓

Where will it be used?
Mainly at home in the living room but it must be portable.

| ANNE SMITH | 3A | STEADY HAND GAME | DATE |

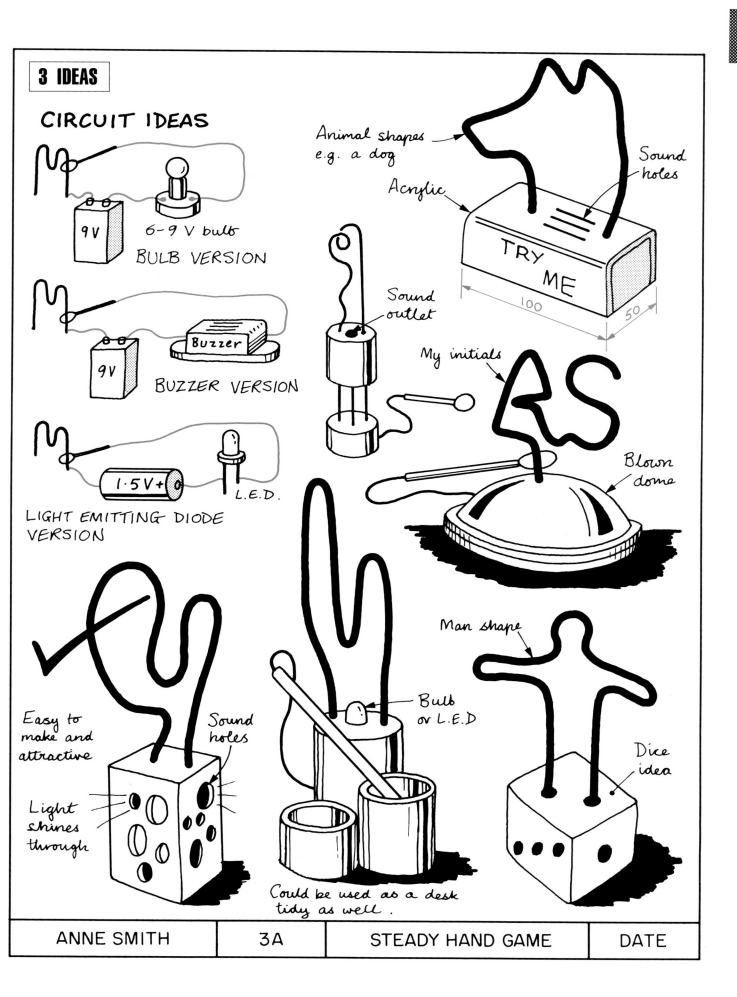

3 IDEAS

CIRCUIT IDEAS

9V

6-9 V bulb

BULB VERSION

9V

Buzzer

BUZZER VERSION

1·5V +

L.E.D.

LIGHT EMITTING DIODE VERSION

Animal shapes e.g. a dog

Acrylic

Sound holes

TRY ME

100

50

Sound outlet

My initials

RS

Blown dome

Easy to make and attractive

Sound holes

Light shines through

Bulb or L.E.D

Man shape

Dice idea

Could be used as a desk tidy as well.

| ANNE SMITH | 3A | STEADY HAND GAME | DATE |

Example 3: A steady hand game (continued)

4 DEVELOPMENT OF BEST IDEA(S)

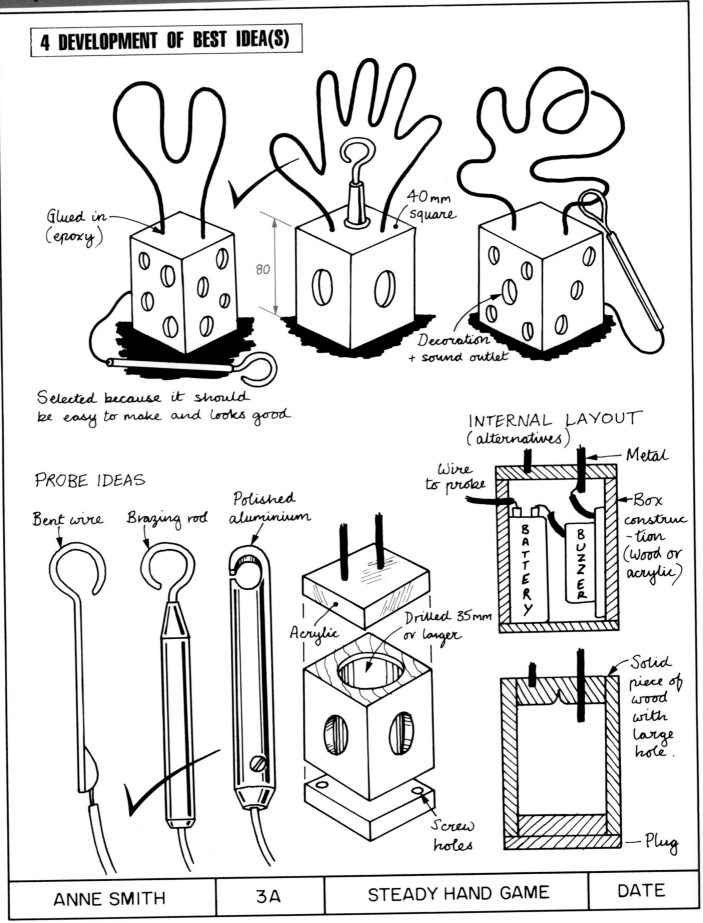

Glued in (epoxy)

40 mm square

80

Decoration + sound outlet

Selected because it should be easy to make and looks good

INTERNAL LAYOUT (alternatives)

Wire to probe

Metal

Box construc-tion (Wood or acrylic)

BATTERY

BUZZER

PROBE IDEAS

Bent wire

Brazing rod

Polished aluminium

Acrylic

Drilled 35mm or larger

Screw holes

Solid piece of wood with large hole.

Plug

| ANNE SMITH | 3A | STEADY HAND GAME | DATE |

5 WORKING DRAWINGS

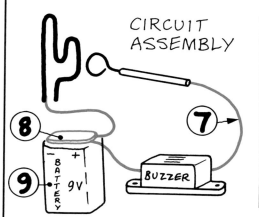

CIRCUIT ASSEMBLY

PART Nº	DESCRIPTION	Nº OFF	MATERIAL	COMMENTS
1	WIRE SHAPE	1	BRASS	GLUED ON
2	PROBE	1	BRASS	+ PEN COVER
3	TOP	1	ACRYLIC	RED (GLUED ON)
4	CONTAINER	1	ASH	VARNISHED
5	BUZZER	1		BOUGHT
6	BASE	1	ACRYLIC	SCREWED ON
7	WIRE	1	P.V.C. COVERED	FLEXIBLE WIRE
8	BATTERY CLIP	1		BOUGHT
9	BATTERY 9 V	1		BOUGHT

PARTS LIST

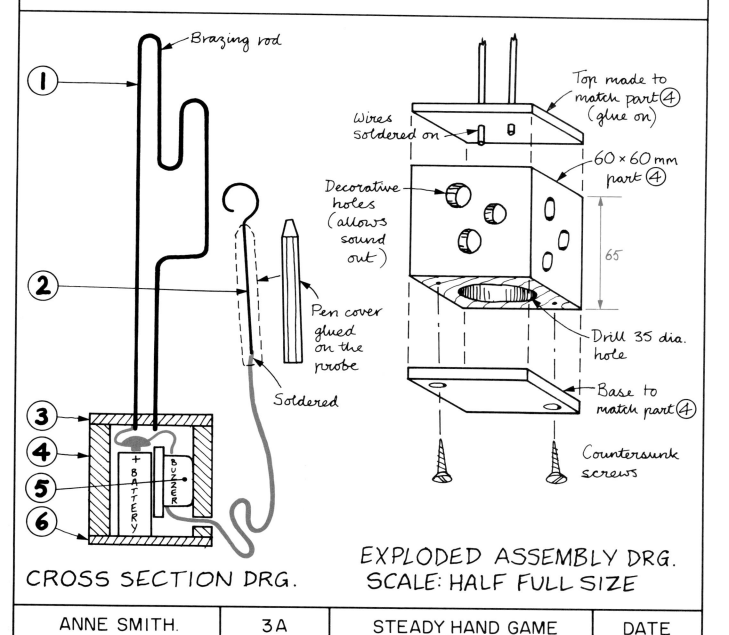

CROSS SECTION DRG.

EXPLODED ASSEMBLY DRG.
SCALE: HALF FULL SIZE

Brazing rod · Wires soldered on · Decorative holes (allows sound out) · Pen cover glued on the probe · Soldered · Top made to match part 4 (glue on) · 60 × 60 mm part 4 · 65 · Drill 35 dia. hole · Base to match part 4 · Countersunk screws

| ANNE SMITH. | 3A | STEADY HAND GAME | DATE |

Example 3: A steady hand game (continued)

6 MAKE

Comments on how it was made

'The steady hand game was made quite quickly working from the **working drawing**. The wire shape was difficult to bend until my teacher showed me how to bend it round a piece of steel rod. It was difficult to soft solder a wire onto the wire shape inside the container. I should have soldered it on before the top was glued in place. The drilling for the large hole in the wood piece was much easier than I expected. I used a 35 mm machine flat bit for the hole. The wood was firmly clamped while drilling.'

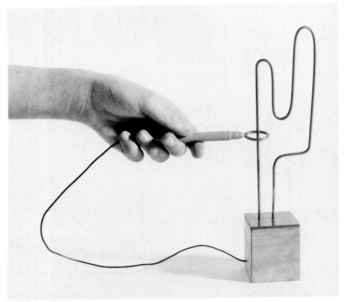

The steady hand game being used.

7 TESTS

STEADY HAND GAME

Comments on the original functions

Fun to use.
It is fun to use and popular with everybody who has used it. The favourite game is to see who can do it the fastest. (Record is 8 seconds)

To look good.
I am pleased with the end result and other people seem to like it too.

To be easy to use.
The probe is comfortable and easy to use but the battery access could be easier.

Comments and possible improvements

1 The buzzer is rather loud if used in a quiet place but just right for use in the school.
2 The base could be a little larger to provide more stability.
3 The bent wire shape could be made more complex.
4 The battery used is rather expensive. An alternative electric system may be cheaper.

Conclusion

I am very happy with the game but it could have been made harder to play and more stable.

EADY HAND GAME	DATE

Ordering parts

It is sometimes a good idea to order the parts you need yourself rather than rely on your teacher to do it for you. Below is a sample letter which will help you.

Notes
- **Use an up-to-date catalogue.**
- **Give a full and accurate description.**
- **Use the firm's code if given.**
- **Add VAT if not already included.**
- **Add packing and postage charges if asked for (check in catalogue).**
- **Keep a copy of the order.**

TO
EXPRESS ELECTRICS
P.O. BOX 3
NEWTOWN
COUNTY.
DATE.

FROM
MISS ANNE SMITH
2 KINGS RD.
SHREWSBURY
COUNTY.

Dear Sir,
    Please could you supply the following parts as described in your latest catalogue.

DESCRIPTION	CODE	PRICE	× NUMBER	= TOTAL
BUZZER	B100A	0.98	1	0.98
BATTERY CLIP	BC12A	0.10	1	0.10
BULBS 6V	BU 6V	0.15	2	0.30
			TOTAL	1.38
			+ VAT	0.20
			+ POST	0.50
				2.08

Cheque enclosed.
Thank you.
Yours faithfully

Miss Anne Smith

THE DESIGN PROCESS
EXPLAINED IN DETAIL

This section is intended to help you when designing any product in school or at home. The design process is explained, together with checklists and examples.

1 BRIEF

The design brief is a short statement of what is to be designed and made. It comes from a **need** that somebody has, or a **problem** that needs solving. The wording of the **brief** needs careful thought. Design briefs are often quite detailed and indicate
- who will use the product (once made).
- where the product will be used (e.g. indoors, outdoors, in the kitchen etc.).
- any restriction placed on the design (e.g. to be as cheap as possible, to be made within two hours, to be a certain size etc.).

Below are examples of **briefs.**

1 BRIEF

Design and make a DESK TIDY to hold pens, pencils, ruler etc. suitable for use on my desk or table. It should not take more than eight workshop sessions to make it.

At present my desk is rather untidy

1 BRIEF

Design and make a DESIGN FOLDER for this year's design work (to include teacher handouts as well).

It must be:
- capable of holding A4 size paper.
- easy to open for marking and attractive.
- made in two practical sessions.
The front cover should have the following information on: name, class, C.D.T. and teacher's name.

2 INVESTIGATION

The **investigation** stage considers the requirements of the design and can only be carried out properly if you are open-minded and prepared to do some basic research.

There are many ways of carrying out an investigation. The method described below has produced some very good designs. It involves going through the following stages:
A The **main functions** are listed.
B Any **questions and comments** are written down.
C Some basic **research** is carried out.
D A **check** is then made against the **investigation checklist** to help ensure important factors are not ignored.
The above stages are now explained in more detail.

A LISTING THE MAIN FUNCTIONS
A list of the main functions (requirements) should be made. It can then be helpful to indicate which you think are the most important functions.

The example below shows a list of **functions.**

2 INVESTIGATION

A FUNCTIONS OF A DESK TIDY

To hold pens, pencils, ruler, rubber, etc.
To look attractive.
To be easy to obtain pens etc.
To be easy to carry about.

B QUESTIONS AND COMMENTS
Now ask yourself questions about the product. The answers and comments you want to make can be placed next to the question, or answered later on when things become clearer.

The following key words should help you think of questions: Who? What? When? Why? How?

Your teacher may have a list of questions s/he wants you to answer.

Below are examples of **questions and comments** used in the investigation.

B QUESTIONS AND COMMENTS

How many pens and pencils should it hold?
What size should it be?
What are the most important sizes?
How should the pens etc. be arranged?
How much can I afford to pay?
What materials are available?
How can it be carried?
Where can I obtain ideas?

2 INVESTIGATION (CONTINUED)

C RESEARCH
RESEARCH is not a separate topic; it should be carried out as and when required. Research can consist of things like: looking at catalogues, measuring basic sizes, finding out what is available in the shops that may be of interest, asking people for their points of view, collecting data etc.

D USING THE CHECKLIST
Go through the checklist below to make sure you have not ignored important factors.
Note These topics are explained in more detail in the next few pages.

```
INVESTIGATION CHECKLIST

 1  Important sizes
 2  Human factors (ergonomics)
 3  Appearance
 4  Strength
 5  Materials (and their finish)
 6  Cost (in money and time)
 7  Safety
 8  Construction (manufacture)
 9  Fittings needed
10  Energy or power needed (if a technological
    project)
11  Other factors.
```

The investigation explained in greater detail

1 IMPORTANT SIZES
Find out what the most important sizes are. The following questions may help:

What, if anything, will be held or enclosed and how big will it need to be?
Does it need to be small for storage purposes?
Will it need to be carried?
Are there any bought parts that have to be measured?
. . . etc.

These are examples of **sizes** that need to be known before designing a desk tidy.

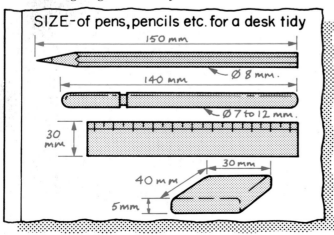

2 HUMAN FACTORS (ERGONOMICS)
The **human factors** that affect our designs need to be considered carefully. **Ergonomics** is a technical word used to describe the human factors. Humans vary in size and shape. They are capable of running, sitting, kneeling etc. Equally, there are things people cannot do such as lift very large loads, see in the dark, or fly. They like to be reasonably comfortable, have their own interests, want to be loved and feel important. Humans change a great deal during their lifetime, so it is important to know for whom you are designing. The needs of a small child are quite different from those of an old person.

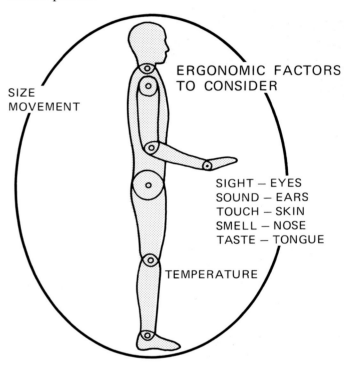

Size
Size needs to be taken into account (e.g. hand or finger sizes may need to be considered).

Movement
Is movement important (e.g. can everything be reached easily)?

Sight (eyes)
Are there parts that need to be seen easily (e.g. controls on a radio)?

Sound (ears)
Is noise likely to be a problem (e.g. squeaks can be very annoying)?

Feel (skin)
The parts touched will need to be comfortable. Sharp edges will need to be removed.

Smell (nose)
Is smell likely to be a problem or an asset?

Taste (tongue)
Some materials can be toxic; do not use them if they might be put in the mouth. Be especially careful if babies and toddlers are involved.

Temperature
Humans do not like to be cold or too hot.

Some ergonomic examples

Adult hand
(approximate size)

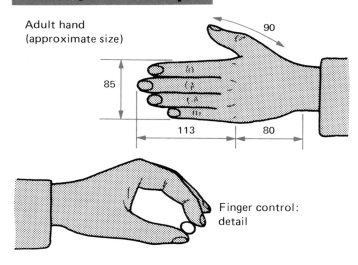

90

85

113   80

Finger control:
detail

Computer workstation. Arrows indicate possible movement to allow for different size users

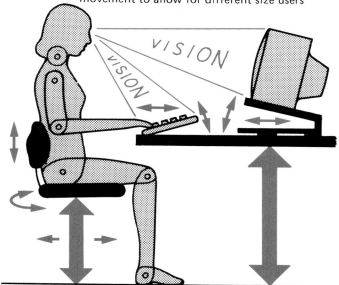

VISION

VISION

Ergonomic
drawings can be
complex
or very
simple

matchstick man

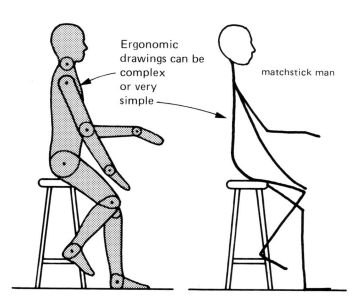

A quickly made card human model to determine some ergonomic factors.

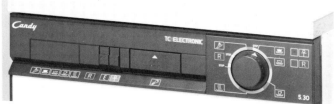

The controls on a Candy electronic dishwasher. Note: The use of clear, concise symbols is important.

Telephones need to be comfortable and easy to use. This one is made by GEC.

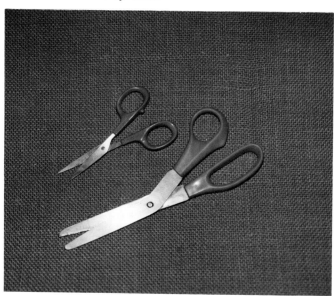

Some scissors have moulded handles so that they are more comfortable to use.

2 INVESTIGATION (CONTINUED)

3 APPEARANCE

The appearance of a product is always important and sometimes it is *the* most important factor. The appearance of any product depends on some or all of the following factors:

> Line, shape or form
>
> Colour
>
> Texture
>
> Decoration

A product's appearance is also affected by the background or place it is used.

Note The section 'Appearance' on pages 29–31 explains the headings above in more detail.

4 STRENGTH

The product being designed must resist the different forces that will act on it. The forces can consist of any of the following types:

Tensile (pulling forces)
Compression (pushing forces)
Shear (cutting forces)
Bending
Twisting

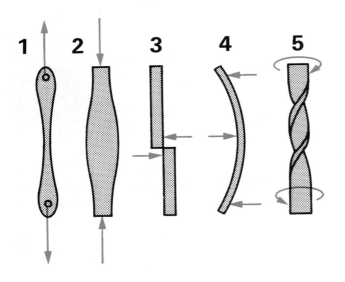

Name the force you think each of these drawings represents.

5 MATERIALS (AND THEIR FINISH)

At this stage it is a good idea to
– list the materials that could be used.
– say why these materials are suitable.
– indicate the kind of surface finish you want.

Note A Turn to pages 45, 46 and 117 for help in **selecting the best materials.**

Note B The weight and life expectancy you want may affect your choice.

6 COST (IN MONEY AND TIME)

You will need to have some idea of the cost and the time that can be spent on your design. Sometimes it is a good idea to buy parts to save time; other times it is better to make a part yourself. What is the maximum cost you can afford or think is sensible for your design?

7 SAFETY

Everything you make needs to be safe in use. The following checklist should help you ensure your design is made safely.

Edges. Sharp edges need to be rounded (except cutting edges).
Stability. The product should be stable to stop it falling over.
Fire risk. Is there likely to be any fire risk?
Electrical dangers. Avoid using **mains** electricity if possible, unless a qualified electrician is able to check it for you. Low voltage batteries, e.g. 9 V batteries, are safe.

8 CONSTRUCTION (MANUFACTURE)

The main methods of **manufacturing** are described on pages 54–65.

Below is a summary which lists the four main ways of making things.

Cutting out. The parts are cut out by sawing, drilling, filing etc.).
Moulding. The parts are moulded by the application of a force to form it (e.g. injection moulding, blow moulding, beaten metalwork, forging etc.).
Casting. A liquid is poured into a prepared mould which then sets hard (e.g. metal casting, plastic embedding, 'plaster of paris' casting).
Fabrication. The form required is made up by parts being joined together (e.g. using screws, bolts, glues, solder etc.).

What method(s) of manufacture do you think is suitable for your design?

9 FITTINGS NEEDED

Sometimes it is worth buying certain parts such as special screws, electrical motors etc., rather than making do with unsatisfactory parts.
These are some questions to ask yourself about fittings:

Are the parts easy to obtain?
When will the parts arrive if ordered?
How much will the parts cost?

10 ENERGY REQUIREMENTS

When designing an electrically powered model or vehicle, it is important to know what type of power supply is needed. Allowances should be made for energy losses due to friction etc.
For more help see pages 103–107.

11 OTHER FACTORS

Is there anything else to consider?
Below are a few possible questions to ask yourself:

Will it be used in the rain or wet?
Where will it be stored?
Will rust or decay be a problem?

3 IDEAS

This stage is done by drawing **ideas** and possible solutions, as shown in the example opposite, together with writing some explanatory notes.

If a good idea comes to you earlier than this stage, make a note of it before you forget it, then include it here.

This stage should *stretch your imagination*. Even seemingly silly ideas should be included; they may turn out to be very original and important.

Note Models are sometimes very useful at this stage. If you need help you could try the following:
- Look at library books, magazines etc.
- Ask other people.
- Visit shops to see what ideas they have.
- Use a method called 'brainstorming', where a group of people sit round and put ideas forward — nobody is allowed to criticise anybody else. Notes and sketches are made at the same time.

4 DEVELOPMENT OF BEST IDEAS

This is done by selecting the **best idea** (or ideas) from the 'ideas' stage you have just considered, and then stating why you selected it. The idea is then developed in detail (example opposite).

The following questions can be used as a checklist to help your 'development of best idea(s)':

- Does the idea selected satisfy the original design brief?
- Is it attractive? Draw it out fully in colour to see what it could look like. This is sometimes called a **presentation drawing.**
- What materials could be used and why?
- Indicate the important sizes.
- How can each part be made?
- What joints could be used?
- What surface finish and texture could be used?

Models and **mock-ups** are sometimes essential at this stage to make sure the best idea satisfies the original need.

Good graphical communication techniques, including the use of colour, should be used. (See pages 34–44 for help with graphical communication techniques.) Sometimes, as the best idea is being developed it becomes obvious that there are problems. If this happens, it may be better to select another idea and develop that instead.

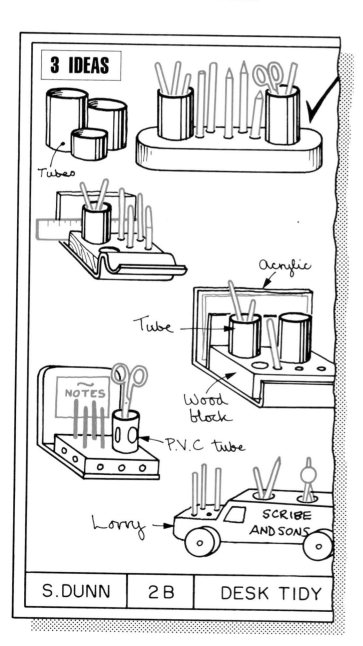

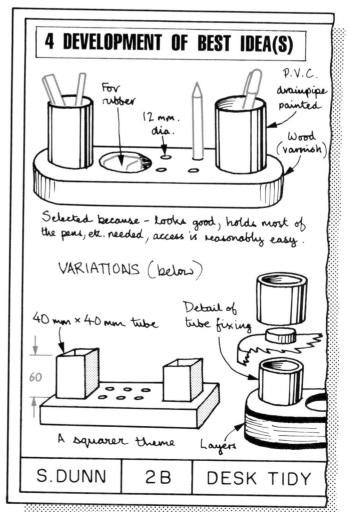

5 WORKING DRAWINGS AND MODELS

A **working drawing** or **working model** is now needed so that the product can be made without much trouble. A working drawing needs to show
– how the parts are assembled.
– all the essential sizes.
– the materials to be used.
– the 'surface finish'.
– the joints to be used.

Working drawings

Two examples of working drawings are given below and opposite. The first example shows two views of a 'desk tidy'. The second example on the next page includes an 'assembly sketch' which makes the drawing easier to understand.

Both examples include a 'Parts list' which makes the drawing easier to work from. Some working drawings also include a 'Cutting list' indicating the length, width and thickness of each piece of material, such as wood, that needs cutting.

Questions about the working drawing illustrated below

Note The worksheet below is reproduced two-thirds of actual size.

1 Which parts are made from wood?
2 How deep are the 12 mm diameter holes?
3 Which part is made from PVC?
4 How high is the tube from the base piece?
5 How many views are drawn?
6 How is part (2) joined to part (3)?

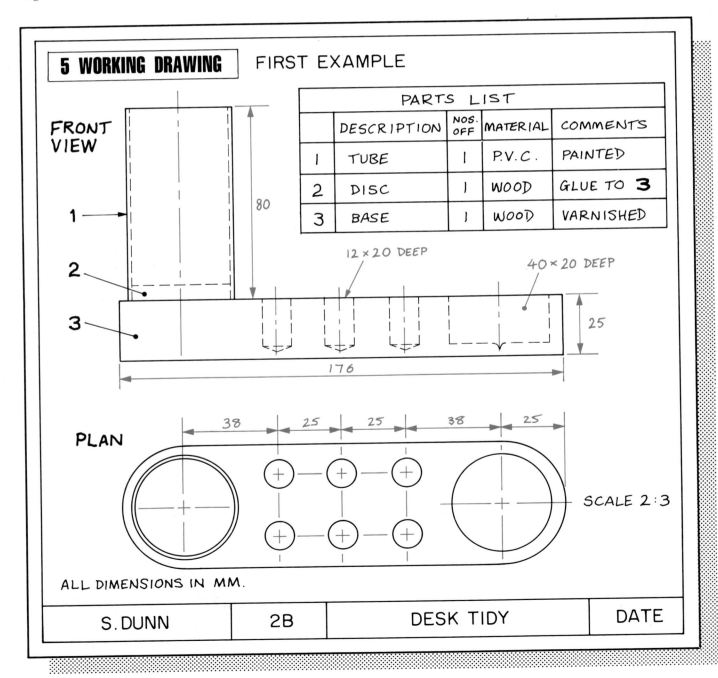

5 WORKING DRAWING — FIRST EXAMPLE

FRONT VIEW

PLAN

PARTS LIST

	DESCRIPTION	NOS. OFF	MATERIAL	COMMENTS
1	TUBE	1	P.V.C.	PAINTED
2	DISC	1	WOOD	GLUE TO **3**
3	BASE	1	WOOD	VARNISHED

80

12 × 20 DEEP

40 × 20 DEEP

25

176

38   25   25   38   25

SCALE 2:3

ALL DIMENSIONS IN MM.

S. DUNN	2B	DESK TIDY	DATE

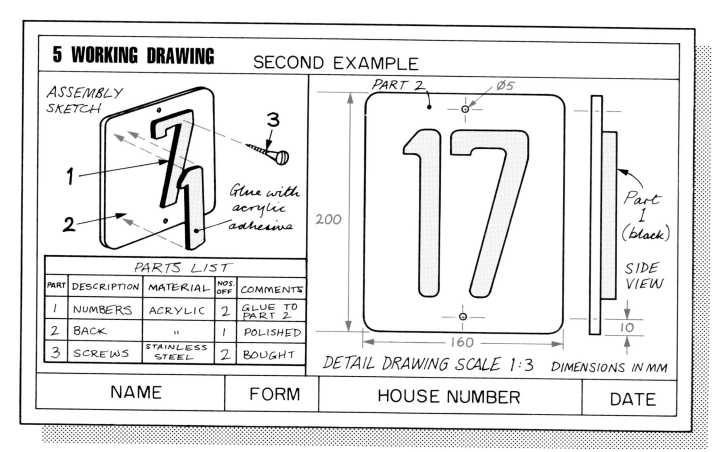

5 WORKING DRAWING SECOND EXAMPLE

ASSEMBLY SKETCH

3

Glue with acrylic adhesive

1
2

PART 2   Ø5

17

200

Part 1 (black)

SIDE VIEW

160   10

DETAIL DRAWING SCALE 1:3   DIMENSIONS IN MM

PARTS LIST				
PART	DESCRIPTION	MATERIAL	NOS. OFF	COMMENTS
1	NUMBERS	ACRYLIC	2	GLUE TO PART 2
2	BACK	"	1	POLISHED
3	SCREWS	STAINLESS STEEL	2	BOUGHT

NAME	FORM	HOUSE NUMBER	DATE

Working models

Working models are sometimes preferred to working drawings.

The advantages of working models
- They are sometimes easier and quicker to produce than technical drawings.
- They can be moved about and viewed from various angles.
- In a model, problems such as stability, ease of use and whether it will work, are usually more obvious.
- Models can be touched.
- Errors are usually obvious and can be corrected.

Note Parts of a design can be modelled separately to check that a particular part works (i.e. to detect any mechanical design problems).

The disadvantages of making models
- Appropriate modelling materials and construction kits are required.
- Safe storage space is needed.
- Copies cannot be made quickly.

MAKING A MODEL
Before making a model you will need to consider
- the size it should be.
- the kind of materials the model should be made from.

MODELLING MATERIALS
When selecting modelling materials it is important to try to use materials with properties similar to the materials you hope to use in the finished product. The following materials are commonly used:

> paper, card, plasticine, clay, wire, strips of wood, balsa-wood, old packaging materials such as drink containers, etc., sheet plastic, foamed plastics such as expanded polystyrene, plaster of paris, construction kits such as LEGO® Technical Kits, Meccano, Fischertechnik etc.

Joints can be made with glue, tape, pins, clips, string and interlocking joints, but of course any method can be used.

Examples of models are shown on the next page.

A selection of modelling materials. Can you think of any more?

Working models (continued): Examples

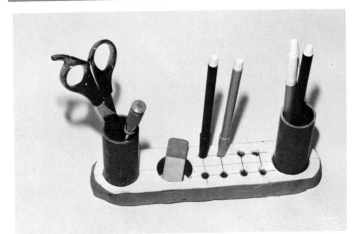

A desk tidy model being tested. It is made from clay, paper and plastic tubes.

A pantograph made by a pupil at school. The model used is shown in the background.

Working models of a digger and a buggy made from LEGO® technical kits.

A pull toy made from acrylic plastic sheet, string and brass paper clips. The drawing shows the rear view and how the string is attached.

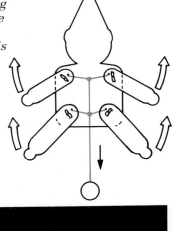

Model sculptures made from expanded polystyrene.

6 MAKE IT

Now it is time to **make** the product you have designed, referring to the **working drawing** or **working model** as and when required. Before starting, ask your teacher to approve your design, and **plan** how you intend to make the individual parts. It is important to realise that some jobs are best done in a certain sequence, for example, it is easier to polish the edges of a piece of plastic (e.g. acrylic) *before* it is bent.

Do *not* be afraid to consider improvements to your design as it is being made, but first ask your teacher to approve the changes needed.

Note Use methods that can make your job quicker to produce, for example, **templates** can make 'marking out' easier.

QUESTIONS TO ASK YOURSELF

What tools will be needed to cut the material?
How will the parts be held while shaping and forming them?
Will a jig or template make the job easier?

For more practical help turn to the section 'Shaping and forming materials' on pages 54–65.

Examples of **equipment** that you may need to use are shown below and right.

A small lathe being used to 'turn down' a tapered point.

A flat bit in a pillar drill drilling a large hole in the base piece of a desk tidy.

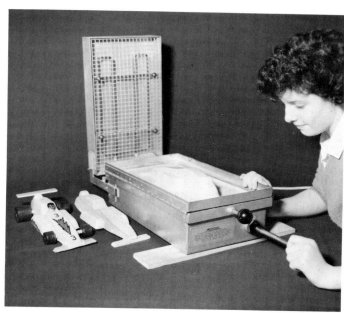

A vacuum former that has been used to form a racing car body. The mould used and finished car are also shown.

A polishing machine being used to polish acrylic plastic.

A universal saw suitable for use by pupils being used to make an elephant jigsaw.

7 TESTING

Once the design has been made it will need testing. There are three main parts in a full and complete test, as follows:

1 Ensure it satisfies the most important functions
You will need to refer back to the original list of functions made at the investigation stage.

2 Record results of any tests or modifications made

3 Suggest possible improvements
— as if it were going to be made again.

Test reports are usually written as notes together with drawings and graphs etc.

Notes
Some testing needs to be done over a period of time. You may only be able to test it in its proper setting.

TYPICAL QUESTIONS LISTED TO HELP YOU
How easy is it to use?
Does it look attractive?
Is it strong enough in use?
Is it safe in use?
Is the construction satisfactory?
Is it easy to maintain in good condition?
Did it cost more than expected?
What tests need to be carried out?
What improvements were made?
What improvements can still be made?
Were the best materials used in construction?

Examples of **projects being tested** are given on this page.

Testing a paper tower made from six pieces of A4 paper. The bathroom scales are used to record the results.

Testing a vehicle designed to climb up as steep a slope as possible (made from a LEGO® technical kit).

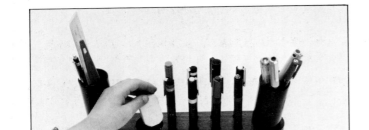

The completed desk tidy. Testing to see if everything fits properly.

The marked scale of the 'fish scales' being tested for accuracy.

Questions about the design process

QUESTIONS ABOUT THE 'INVESTIGATION' STAGE
1 List at least four important functions you think a family car must fulfil.
2 List five functions an electric kettle must fulfil.
3 What human factors need to be considered in the design of a bicycle? Consider the seat, the brakes and the pedals in turn.

QUESTIONS ABOUT THE 'IDEAS' STAGE
1 Sketch three possible **ideas** of a toy suitable for use in the bath by a three-year-old child.
2 Sketch three possible **ideas** suitable for a game that makes use of either a magnet, or marbles, or an elastic band.

QUESTIONS ABOUT 'WORKING DRAWINGS' AND MODELS
1 Make a working drawing of something you have made recently. Two views are required, e.g. front view and a plan view.
2 Using a sheet of cardboard and some glue, make a model of a radio or of a board game.

QUESTION ON 'TESTING'
Test a felt-tip pen and a ball-point pen on various surfaces and in different conditions. Record results in a visual way, for instance as a graph.

APPEARANCE

This section is about the visual elements that need to be considered when designing. A product's appearance is sometimes the most important factor to the user or purchaser, for example fashion items such as clothes and shoes, and occasionally ordinary products such as cars, etc. This section is divided up as follows:

1 **Lines, shapes and forms** (pages 29–31)
2 **Texture** (page 31)
3 **Pattern and style** (page 32)
4 **Colour** (page 33)

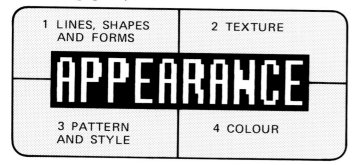

1 LINES, SHAPES AND FORMS	2 TEXTURE
APPEARANCE	
3 PATTERN AND STYLE	4 COLOUR

1 LINES, SHAPES OR FORMS

Each of these words is described below.

Lines

Lines are basic to all drawings; they can also be added to products in order to provide information or as decoration.

Various effects produced with lines.

The feeling of movement is produced by the way these lines are drawn.

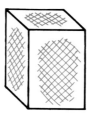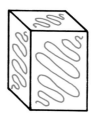

Lines applied to containers for decorative purposes only.

Lines used to produce face shapes.

Shapes and forms

Products having *two* dimensions are said to be **shapes**; triangles and hexagons are examples. The two dimensions of a **shape** are **length** and **width**.

Forms have **depth** as well as length and width, and are said to be **three dimensional**; examples include cubes and spheres.

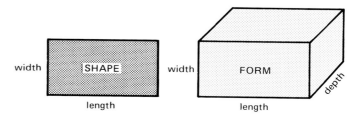

Shapes and forms are sometimes divided up into categories such as **geometric** and **natural** (or **organic**).

Geometric shapes and forms are precise and can be drawn with instruments.

Natural (or **organic**) shapes and forms such as animals and plants are not as precise and are usually drawn or made by hand without the use of instruments.

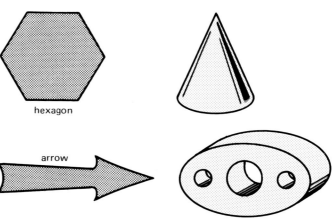

Geometric shapes and forms — see technical drawing books for more examples.

Ideas for some natural shapes and forms

Using shapes and forms in design work

The following shapes and forms are grouped together to allow you to see the effects that can be produced using certain methods. If stuck for a shape or form idea, you could use some of the following methods.

RANDOM METHOD
Lines are sketched onto a piece of paper, then any interesting shapes are selected and coloured in.

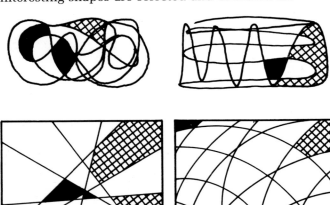

CUTTING AND REARRANGING PIECES
A picture or drawing is cut up and rearranged.

ENLARGING A SHAPE
One way of enlarging a shape is to divide the shape up, then transfer the shape square by square to a larger grid.

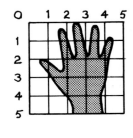
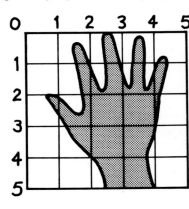

POSITIVE AND NEGATIVE SHAPES

These are like mirror images about a line with the other half coloured in the opposite (negative) way.

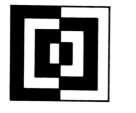

CONTRASTING SHAPES

The shapes contrast in one way or another, for example the smooth circle is contrasted with a pointed triangle in the upper right drawing.

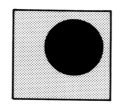
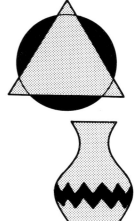

SHAPES IN HARMONY

Shapes in harmony are similar.

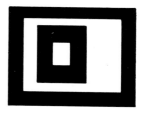

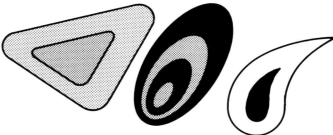

SIMPLIFIED SHAPES

These shapes have been simplified. Can you tell what they are supposed to represent?

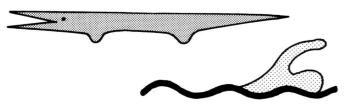

2 TEXTURE

Texture is the surface finish found on all materials. When you are designing it is important to select the best surface finish for a particular job. A soft smooth chair is far more comfortable than a hard rough chair. Textures are described as being hard, soft, rough or smooth.

Diamond ring
(hard and smooth)

Glove (soft and smooth texture)

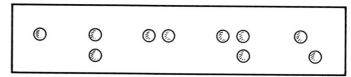

ABCDE in braille (raised dots), as used by blind people to read.

3 PATTERN AND STYLE

Pattern

Patterns vary enormously, from very complex coloured patterns to very simple ones. They are often applied to products for 'effect' to make them more attractive or to disguise something. Products to which patterns are applied include—

wallpaper, tiles, and packaging materials.

PATTERNS BASED ON A TRIANGULAR GRID

PATTERNS BASED ON CIRCLES

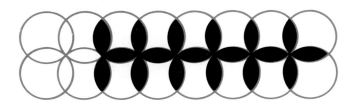

PATTERNS MADE BY REARRANGING LETTERS

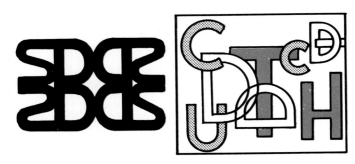

PATTERNS BASED ON LEAF SHAPES

STENCILS AND TEMPLATES

To reproduce a simple shape quickly, a template or a stencil can be cut out and used as shown.

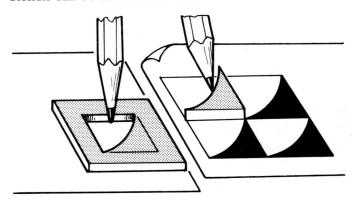

USING A BASIC UNIT TO MAKE A PATTERN

Patterns can be built up as shown by rearranging the basic unit on a prepared grid.

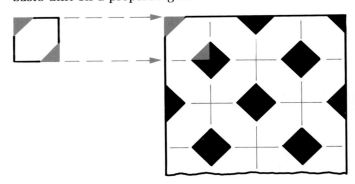

Style

The style that we like now will probably be considered old-fashioned by people in the near future. The question What determines style? is not an easy one to answer but usually involves one of the following:

the time or age the product was made; the person who made or designed it; the technology and the materials available to make it.

Styles from different periods are shown below.

Classical pillars   Old English lettering and numbers

Art Nouveau

1980s punk

4 COLOUR

The appearance of an object can be completely changed by colouring. Would you drink green milk or wash with black soap? We get used to objects being a particular colour and, as designers, we can make use of this. For example, when designing water taps it would be sensible to colour code the hot water tap with red, and the cold water tap with blue.

The colour circle

A **colour circle** helps us understand the relationships between the different **'painting' colours**. On the rear cover of this book is a colour circle. Below is a copy in black and white for easy reference.

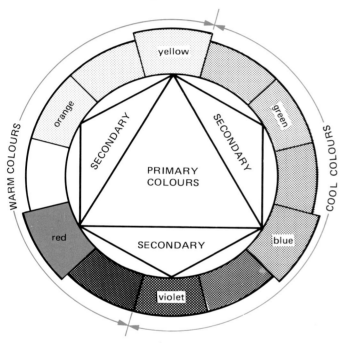

Only the *three* primary colours, **red, blue** and **yellow**, are needed to produce the colour circle. The secondary colours are each a mixture of two primary colours, e.g. blue and yellow make green. Mixing a primary colour, e.g. yellow, with a secondary colour, e.g. green, produces an intermediate colour, e.g. light green.

Colours are sometimes described as –

   warm or **cool** colours.
   dark or **light** colours.
   contrasting or **harmonious** colours.

WARM AND COOL COLOURS

These are marked on the colour circle above with arrows. The warm colours include yellow, red and orange. The cool colours include blue and green.

DARK AND LIGHT COLOURS

By adding 'black' to a colour we produce a **darker** colour, sometimes called a darker **shade**. By adding 'white' to a colour we produce a **paler** colour.

CONTRASTING AND HARMONIOUS COLOURS

Contrasting colours
The biggest contrast is obtained by selecting opposite colours on the colour circle.

Harmonious colours
The colours on either side of a particular colour on the colour circle, are said to be 'in harmony'.

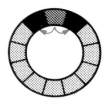

Mixing of colours using light

The mixing of **colours produced by light** is different from that of paint colours. A summary is given below (physics books often explain this in more detail).

The three primary colours for light are **red, green** and **blue**. It is important that you know the difference between primary painting colours and primary light colours, the latter being used for stage lighting, computer graphics, photography etc.

If the three primary colours for light shine on a white screen, the centre where the colours overlap will be **white**, i.e. red, green and blue added together make white.

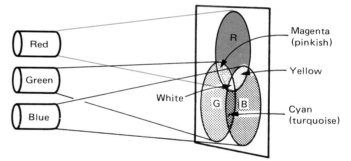

SPLITTING UP A BEAM OF WHITE LIGHT WITH A GLASS PRISM

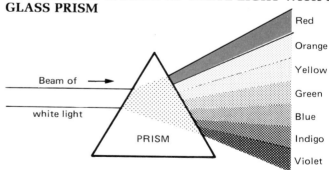

Note The colours of the rainbow are the same (the sunrays are split up by the rain droplets).

Exercises

1 Draw and paint a 'colour circle' similar to the one on the rear cover.
2 Draw three cube shapes then paint them using (a) primary colours, (b) cool colours, (c) harmonious colours.
3 Make several card **spinning tops**, paint each half in a different colour, then mix the colours by spinning them, noting the new colours.

This page illustrates the *graphical communication* methods that are explained in more detail on the next few pages. They are as follows.

1 **Technical sketching methods** (page 35)
2 **Pictorial (or three-dimensional) drawings** (pages 36–37)
3 **Orthographic (or flat) drawings** (pages 38–39)
4 **Sectioning** (page 40)

A lorry is used in examples on this page of the first three drawing methods, so that comparisons can be made between the different methods.

1 Look at the drawings below and see if you can spot the main differences.
2 Which method do you think looks the most realistic and which the least realistic?
3 Which method do you think is the easiest to draw accurately? (Clue: consider wheels.)

Note **Models** are also a very important method used in graphical communication. (See pages 25 and 26 for examples of models.)

SKETCHING

A sketched lorry

ORTHOGRAPHIC OR FLAT DRAWINGS

Four separate views are shown.

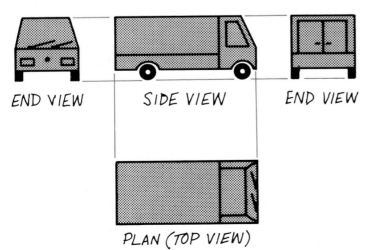

END VIEW   SIDE VIEW   END VIEW

PLAN (TOP VIEW)

PICTORIAL (OR THREE-DIMENSIONAL) DRAWINGS

Pictorial drawings are usually drawn in either of the following: **Oblique, Isometric** or **Perspective.**

Oblique drawing

Isometric drawing

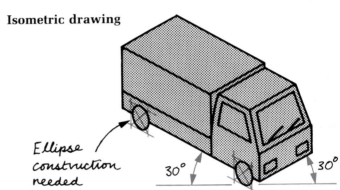

Ellipse construction needed

Perspective drawing

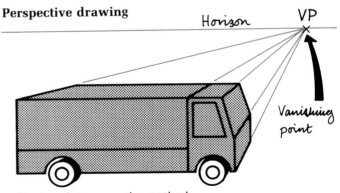

Single point perspective method

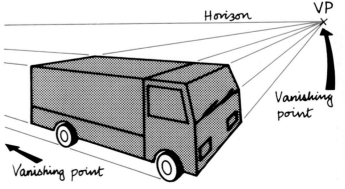

Two point perspective method

1 TECHNICAL SKETCHING METHODS

Sketches are used to quickly communicate thoughts and ideas in design work. Use HB pencils; they produce dark lines which can be rubbed out easily if required. Harder pencils such as the H and 2H types are used mainly for instrument drawing. To help sketch accurately, three methods are described below:

The **centre line** method
The **box** (or **crate**) method
The **grid** method (e.g. using squared paper)

The centre line method of sketching

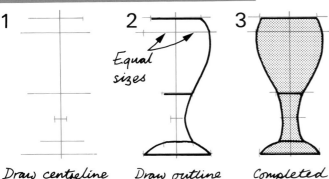

Sketching a goblet (centre line method)

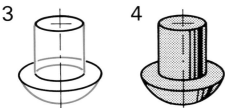

Sketching a rivet (centre line method)

The box method of sketching

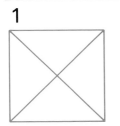

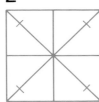

Steps in sketching a circle

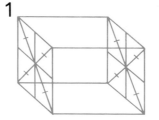
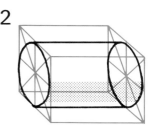

Sketching a cylinder (box method)

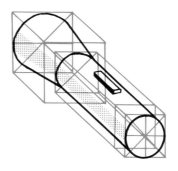

Sketching a torch (box method)

The grid method of sketching

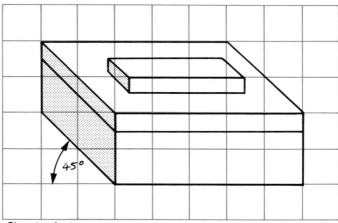

Sketch of a box using squared grid paper

Table sketched using isometric grid paper

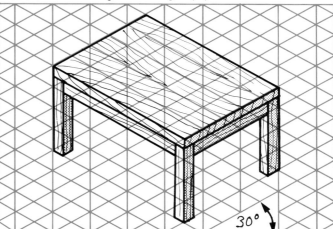

2 PICTORIAL (OR THREE-DIMENSIONAL) DRAWINGS

Pictorial drawings show an object in three dimensions. The methods most commonly used for pictorial drawings are **oblique**, **isometric** and **perspective**.

Oblique drawing

This method is the easiest to use because it starts with a single flat front view. The main advantage is that it can be drawn by direct measurement. The disadvantage is that the drawings are not as realistic as perspective drawings.

Note If circles are to be drawn, try to arrange them on the front view so that they can be drawn using compasses.

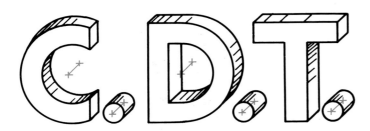

THE STAGES IN DRAWING OBLIQUE FORMS
(a) Draw the front view of the object.
(b) Draw 45-degree lines back as shown.
(c) Measure the depth on the 45-degree lines. (The use of 'half full scale' will obtain a more realistic effect.)
(d) Complete the form and line in as shown below.

(a)

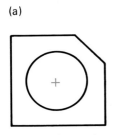

(b)

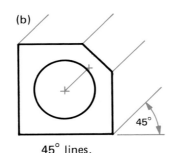

Draw the front view.   45° lines.

(c)

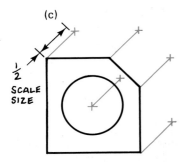

(d)

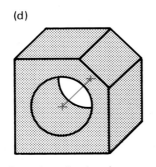

Measure the depth.   Complete the drawing.

Isometric drawing

This method looks more natural than oblique drawing, with one corner of the object in front yet still allowing direct measurement to be made. Curved shapes are more difficult to draw. A compass cannot be used for circles; they have to be constructed or drawn in with an isometric template.

STAGES IN DRAWING IN ISOMETRIC
(a) Draw a vertical line and mark off the height of the object.
(b) Draw the two 30-degree lines using a 30-degree set square, and measure the lengths off as shown.
(c) Draw the other vertical and 30-degree lines as required.
(d) Complete the drawing and line in.

(a)   (b)

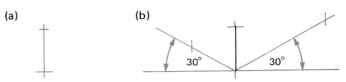

(c)   (d)

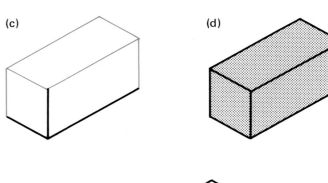

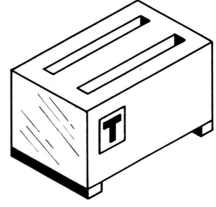

A toaster drawn in isometric

STAGES IN DRAWING CURVES IN ISOMETRIC

Draw 'true shape', with rectangle drawn round and divided up.

1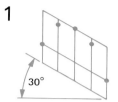

Draw one isometric side and divide up as in true shape.

2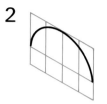

Sketch in curve.

3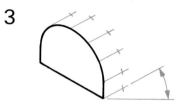

Draw 30° lines as shown, then mark off depth.

4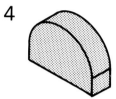

Complete and line in.

One-point perspective (estimated method)

This is a simple but very effective way of drawing (depth is estimated). A flat 'front view' is drawn first.

The example below shows the effect of varying the objects' positions in relationship to the vanishing point (VP).

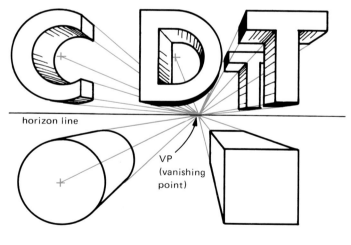

horizon line

VP (vanishing point)

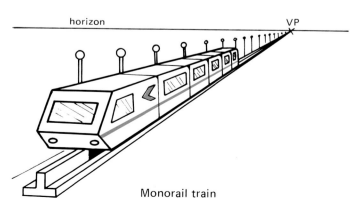

horizon   VP

Monorail train

STAGES IN DRAWING ONE-POINT PERSPECTIVE

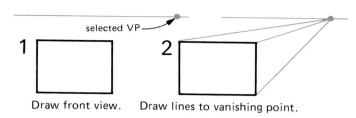

1 Draw front view.

2 Draw lines to vanishing point.

selected VP

3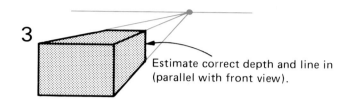

Estimate correct depth and line in (parallel with front view).

Two-point perspective

This is similar to one-point (or single-point) perspective except that there are two vanishing points and the object is viewed from a corner.

Example of two-point perspective.

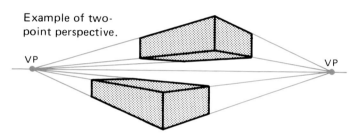

VP   VP

STAGES IN DRAWING TWO-POINT PERSPECTIVE

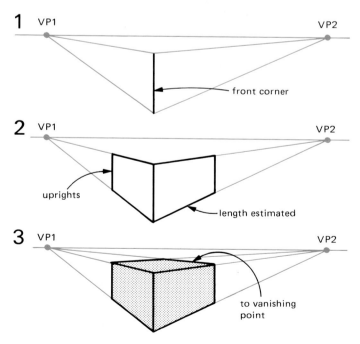

1 VP1   VP2

front corner

2 VP1   VP2

uprights

length estimated

3 VP1   VP2

to vanishing point

Exercises

1 Draw a cube in oblique, isometric and perspective.
2 Draw the letter D in isometric (construct the curve).
3 Draw your initials in oblique and perspective.
4 Draw a lorry in oblique (see page 34 for help).

3 ORTHOGRAPHIC (OR FLAT) DRAWINGS

Orthographic drawing (sometimes called flat or multi-view drawing) is a method of accurately drawing an object from several directions, each view drawn as though it was flat. The views commonly drawn are: **front view, plan view** (or top view), and **end view** (or side view), but other views can be drawn. For example a drawing of an aeroplane may require an underneath view as well, to show the landing wheels clearly.

There are two variations of orthographic **projection** used throughout the world: **first-angle projection** and **third-angle projection**. The only difference is the way the views are drawn on the paper. **First-angle projection** only is explained in this book.

The drawing below shows how the different flat views are obtained; the arrows indicate where the person views the object.

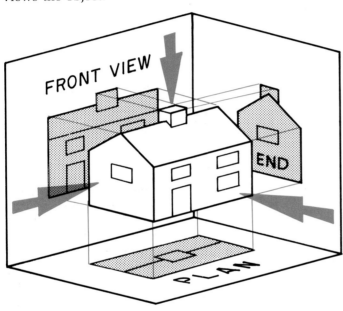

The **orthographic drawing** is laid out flat below. Can you pair up the same views on the drawings above and below?

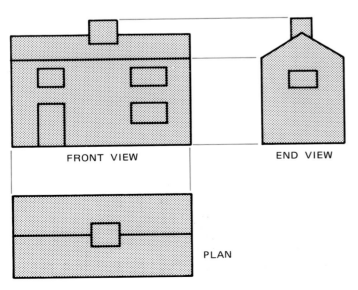

Stages in drawing in orthographic projection

(a) Decide on the sizes (scale) needed to fit the view on the paper (allow room for construction lines etc.).

(b) Draw the front view.

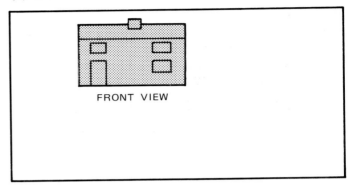

(c) Project faint lines from the front view as shown.

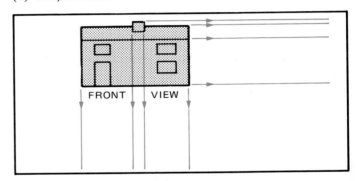

(d) Draw the plan view using the faint lines to help you as shown.

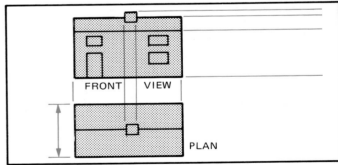

(e) Draw a diagonal line at 45 degrees from the corner as shown; this is used to transfer sizes to the end view from the plan. The end view can then be completed using the information provided by the other two views.

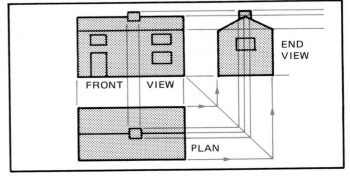

Orthographic projection

ELECTRIC CAR SKETCHES

These are on square graph paper in first-angle projection.

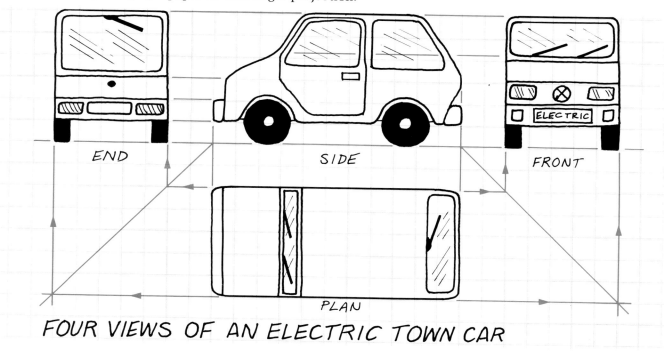

FOUR VIEWS OF AN ELECTRIC TOWN CAR

JEWELLERY CONTAINER

Note the use of cross-section X—X, dimensions and hidden detail.

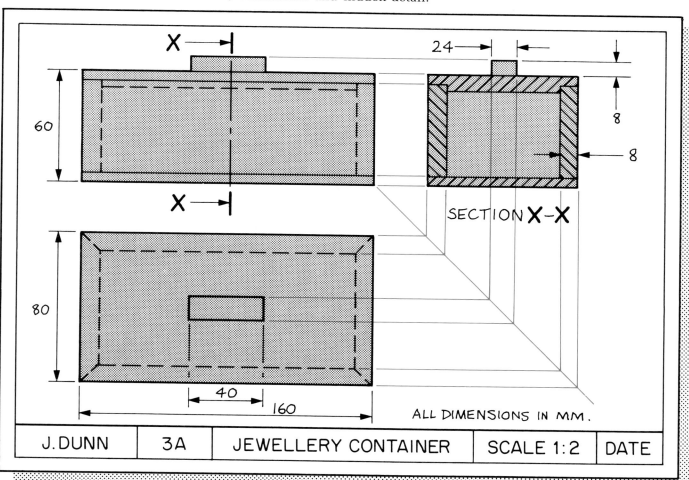

4 SECTIONING

Sectioning allows us to show what an object would look like inside if cut. Below are examples: solid parts are cross-hatched at 45 degrees. Lines A—A and B—B indicate where the object is sectioned. A few things such as holes, nuts and bolts are **not** sectioned.

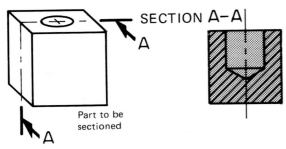

SECTION A—A

Part to be sectioned

Section shows depth of drilled hole.

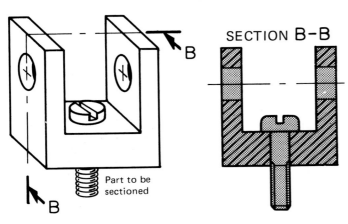

SECTION B—B

Part to be sectioned

Exercises

1 Draw a front view, a side view and a plan view of one of the following: (a) a radio, (b) a televison, (c) a computer, or (d) a calculator.

2 Draw a front view, a plan and an end view (as indicated by the arrows) of the nest box or the toaster below. Supply any missing dimensions. Use A4 size paper.

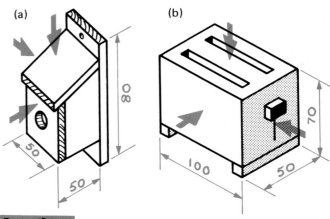

(a)

(b)

Questions

— about the 'door bolt' drawing below

1 Identify the 'front view' (which is cross-sectioned), the 'end view' and the 'plan'.
2 What scale is used for this drawing?
3 What method of projection is used?
4 Why are some parts of the sectional view not cross-hatched?
5 What extra information could be added to this drawing?

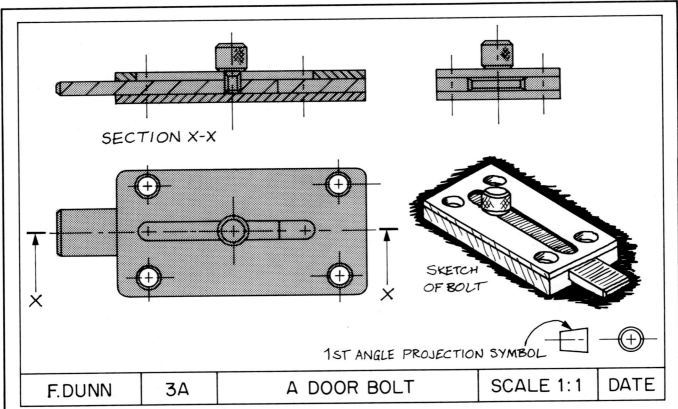

SECTION X-X

SKETCH OF BOLT

1ST ANGLE PROJECTION SYMBOL

| F.DUNN | 3A | A DOOR BOLT | SCALE 1:1 | DATE |

ENGINEERING DRAWING STANDARDS

In our modern technological society, common drawing standards are necessary to avoid confusion in industry and commerce. Booklets are published explaining the standards that have been agreed on in this country by the British Standards Institute. Your teacher may have a British Standards booklet covering drawing standards for use in schools. This page illustrates some of the engineering drawing standards which are useful when making a working drawing.

TYPES OF LINE USED

Outlines

For dimensions, projection and hatching lines

For hidden details

For centre lines

Section lines

To represent a break

PRINTING

When printing letters and numbers it is important that they can be clearly seen; printing is therefore recommended.

ABCDEFGHIJKLM
NOPQRSTUVWXYZ
123456789

Examples of good and bad printing

20 mm
SECTION

20 mm
section

DIMENSIONING

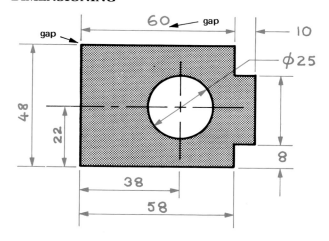

Dimensioned according to British Standards

Dimensioning radii, circles and holes

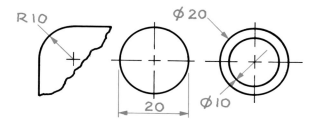

Dimensioning pictorial views

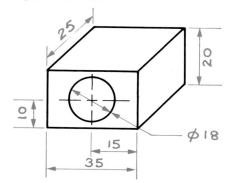

Thread conventions

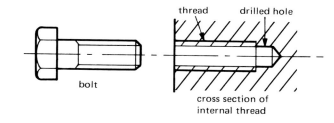

bolt

thread   drilled hole

cross section of
internal thread

Cross section of a wheel and washer

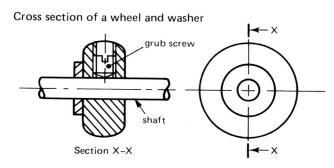

grub screw

shaft

Section X–X

Notes about cross-sectioning

- Shafts and bolts are not sectioned.
- Adjoining parts (the washer and wheel) are cross-sectioned in opposite directions as shown above.

Exercise

Dimension the following shape according to British Standards. Use a ruler to obtain the actual sizes.

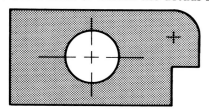

GRAPHICAL PRESENTATION

Good presentation is extremely important nowadays. We expect products to be attractive as well as functional. This section illustrates various techniques that can be used to present technical design drawings in a clear concise way.

PRESENTATION AIDS

It is important to select the appropriate pen, pencil and other aids if good graphical presentation work is to be achieved. The range of equipment available varies from pencils to computer aided design equipment. Some of the basic aids are shown below. Can you think of others?

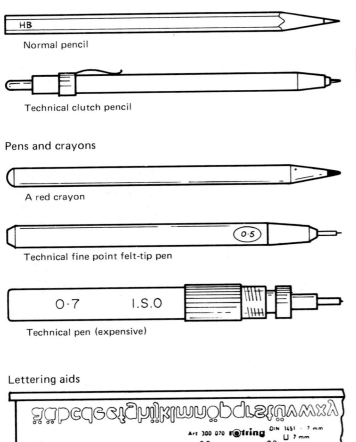

Pencils

Normal pencil

Technical clutch pencil

Pens and crayons

A red crayon

Technical fine point felt-tip pen

Technical pen (expensive)

Lettering aids

Stencil

Dry rub-on transfers

Various aids being used to produce well presented drawings.

PRESENTATION METHODS

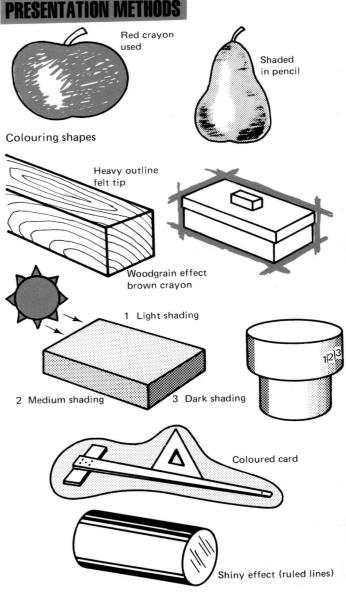

Red crayon used

Shaded in pencil

Colouring shapes

Heavy outline felt tip

Woodgrain effect brown crayon

1 Light shading

2 Medium shading   3 Dark shading

Coloured card

Shiny effect (ruled lines)

Border added to name

Double mounted with coloured card

Ground shaded in

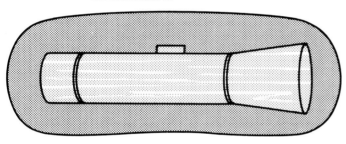

Wide felt-tip pen (light colours) are used with a ruler. The torch shape was then cut out and remounted on card.

Letters and numbers

Letters and numbers are used in all aspects of designing to convey written information and promote the correct image. For example the sign of an antique shop would look wrong if it was written in a modern style. A range of various styles is shown below. For a wider selection see a dry transfer catalogue.

Antiques **TRENDY**

LINKED STENCIL

Croissant *BALLOON*

Signs and symbols

Signs and symbols enable people to understand information very quickly and are becoming more popular as a method of communication.

DIRECTION SIGNS

Can you think of where you could find the signs shown above?

ROAD SIGNS

Road signs are standardised in most countries. Do you know what the signs above mean?

PICTOGRAPHS

Pictographs are based on outlines or known symbols. What do the above pictographs mean?

COMPUTER GRAPHICS

In computer graphics, pictures are made up from individual 'pixels' which can be moved about the screen.

A COMPANY'S IDENTITY

A company's symbol (logo) is shown here as it is used for the company's products, transport and letter headings.

Human model (ergonome)

The human model shown below can be copied by tracing to produce human shapes in sitting positions, etc. This is a good way to make sure that correct sizes are considered when designing furniture, etc.

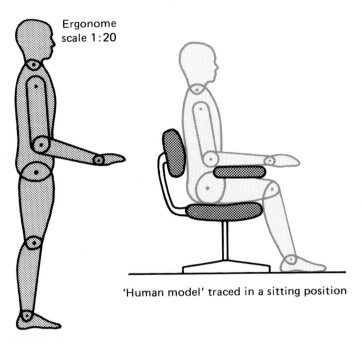

Ergonome
scale 1:20

'Human model' traced in a sitting position

Developments

A development is a flat shape which when folded up produces a useful product such as the soap tray shown below.

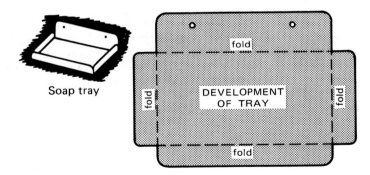

Soap tray

DEVELOPMENT
OF TRAY

Block diagrams

Block diagrams are used to explain complex processes. Below a stereo record player is shown as an example.

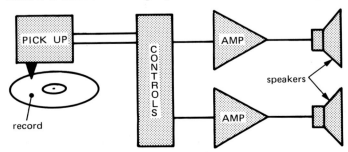

Stereo record player block diagram

Drawn instructions with few words

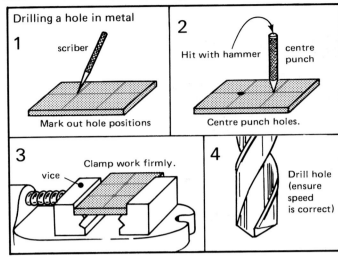

Drilling a hole in metal

1 scriber — Mark out hole positions

2 Hit with hammer — centre punch — Centre punch holes.

3 vice — Clamp work firmly.

4 Drill hole (ensure speed is correct)

Simplification of shapes

Cutting and rearranging shapes

A room plan

1 m grid

bed — wardrobe — window — desk — door

My bedroom

Exercises

1 Design two possible design-folder covers for your current work.

2 Draw an ergonome person sitting in an easy chair which is leaning back at 45 degrees. (Using thin paper, a tracing can be taken from this book.)

3 Collect a paper container, e.g. toothpaste packet, and carefully open it out. Then make a copy of the development, redesign the outside and fold it up again.

4 Using the 'instructions with few words' above as an example, select a process or set of instructions that could be treated in a similar manner, e.g. brazing, or making a cup of tea.

5 Make a block diagram suitable for a tape recorder which will include the following: tape, tapehead, controls, amplifier and speaker.

MATERIALS

SELECTING MATERIALS

In the past mankind had a limited selection of materials to choose from. You will have heard about the Stone Age, the Bronze Age, the Iron Age and the way it changed people's lives. Nowadays we have an enormous range of materials to choose from. It is important that we are able to select the best material for a particular use.

SELECTING THE BEST MATERIAL

In order to select the best material for a particular situation, we need to consider the following:

1 the **physical properties needed**,
2 the **cost**,
3 **shaping and forming** methods,
4 **availability**.

Below is a checklist which will help you select the best material for a particular job.

SELECTING THE BEST MATERIAL (A CHECKLIST)

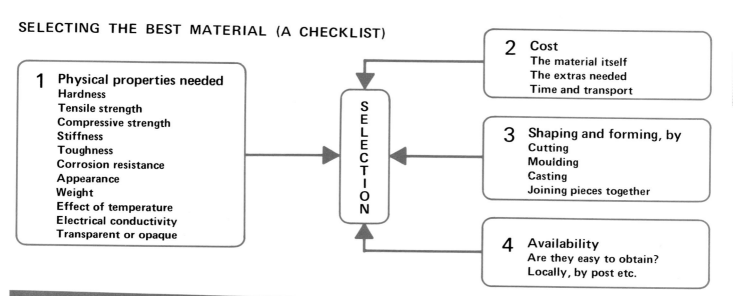

1 Physical properties needed
Hardness
Tensile strength
Compressive strength
Stiffness
Toughness
Corrosion resistance
Appearance
Weight
Effect of temperature
Electrical conductivity
Transparent or opaque

2 Cost
The material itself
The extras needed
Time and transport

3 Shaping and forming, by
Cutting
Moulding
Casting
Joining pieces together

4 Availability
Are they easy to obtain?
Locally, by post etc.

SELECTION

Questions to ask yourself about materials

1 PHYSICAL PROPERTIES NEEDED

Hardness – How hard should the material be to resist wear? For example, a knife sharpener must be harder than the knife, the knife must be harder than the material it is going to cut.

Tensile strength – Will the material need to resist pulling forces?

Compressive strength – Will the material need to resist pushing forces that tend to squash it?

Stiffness – Do you require a rigid shape or form? *Note* The shape and form a material has will affect the stiffness, e.g. a tube of paper is much stiffer than a flat sheet of paper.

Toughness – Will it have to withstand being knocked about? If it will, do not choose a brittle material.

Corrosion resistance – How important is it that the material resists corrosion, rotting etc.?

Appearance – Is the material's natural appearance important, and what surface finish do you want, if any?

Weight – Is the weight of the material critical, e.g. fishing weights would be useless if made from a light plastic.

Effect of temperature – Will the material need to be a good insulator and resist heat or cold?

Electrical conductivity – Will any of the parts need to allow electricity to flow through?

Transparent – Will you need to see through it?

2 WHAT COST?

Schools are mainly concerned with the cost of metal, wood or plastic used, but sometimes you will need to consider the extra costs involved such as: paint, varnish, transfers, postage, new tools needed etc.

3 SHAPING AND FORMING

Materials can be formed by –

Cutting out. Will the material need to be reduced in size by removing pieces using – a drill, a lathe, a saw, a file etc.?

Moulding. Can the material be moulded into the required form using techniques such as – vacuum forming, plastic injection moulding, wood laminating or 'laying up' on a mould with Glass Reinforced Plastics?

Casting. Can the shape or form be cast, e.g. aluminium casting, candle making and plastic casting (embedding)?

Joining pieces together (fabrication). Would it be easier to make the shape up from different pieces using methods such as – nailing, screwing, gluing, riveting etc.?

4 AVAILABILITY

Can the materials be obtained from the school's storeroom or will they have to be bought? Sometimes special sizes are required and will need to be ordered or bought locally.

EXERCISES ABOUT MATERIALS

1 Why do you think the plug, the pan and the kitchen unit have been made from the materials indicated below?

Example
If an electric light bulb had been drawn, a typical answer would be that the glass part is selected because it allows light to pass through and the metal parts at the end are selected because they can pass electricity. Both materials must be resistant to the heat of the filament.

hard rubber cover

brass pin

plastic handle

aluminium

stainless steel sink

plastic covered chipboard

2a What do you think are the two most important 'material properties' each of the following products should have? (Refer to the previous page for help under the heading 1 Physical properties needed.)

2b What material(s) would you select for the shoe, the tray and the tap? (They are to be factory made.)

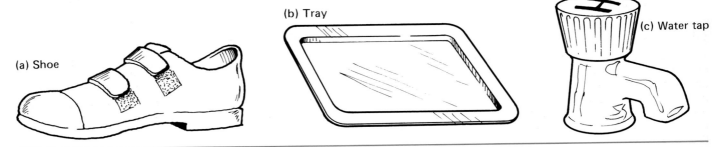

(a) Shoe

(b) Tray

(c) Water tap

3 Below are eleven products and opposite is a list of eleven properties. Match the products with the properties given. Only use each property once, e.g. the **centre punch** must be **hard**.

Materials properties list
Transparent. Electrical conductivity. Hard (already used for the centre punch). Tensile strength. Resistance to high temperature. Compressive strength. Good appearance. Weight. Stiffness. Toughness. Corrosion resistance.

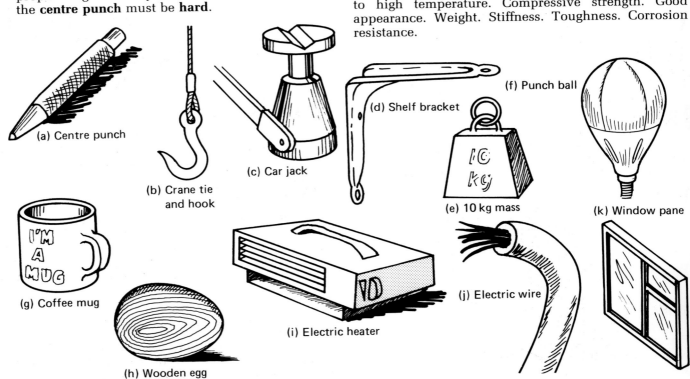

(a) Centre punch

(b) Crane tie and hook

(c) Car jack

(d) Shelf bracket

(e) 10 kg mass

(f) Punch ball

(g) Coffee mug

(h) Wooden egg

(i) Electric heater

(j) Electric wire

(k) Window pane

MATERIALS TESTING

This page illustrates some simple ways of testing materials which you can try. Your school may be lucky enough to have professional testing equipment which you can use as well. Before starting any tests you will need to obtain some test pieces. If possible, use the same sizes in each test so that direct comparisons can be made. The results of each test can be presented as a bar chart.

Hardness

The test pieces for this can be any material more than 4 mm thick. The weight is dropped onto the ball bearing which in turn makes a dent in the test piece; the harder the material, the smaller the dent made.

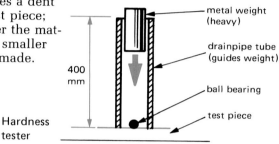

Stiffness

The amount of stiffness is indicated by the degree of deflection made when a load is added. One way to compare materials is to add weights until the material is deflected a certain amount (say 20 mm). The bigger the load required to deflect it, the stiffer the test piece is. It is very important that all the test pieces are exactly the same size.

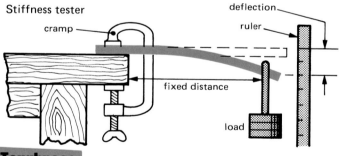

Toughness

This is the resistance to impact. Wear goggles and stand back when testing. Record the number of degrees the hammer swings after it has broken the test piece.

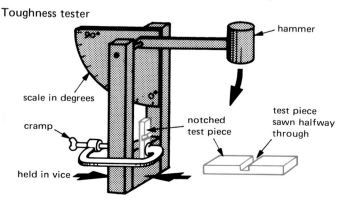

Tensile strength

The device shown below will test thin wires, e.g. copper wire, binding wire, aluminium wire, brazing rod, and piano wire etc. Record two sets of results:
(a) the **force** required to break it in newtons (N), and
(b) the amount of **stretch** or **strain** (see formulas below). (1 kg = 10 N approx.)

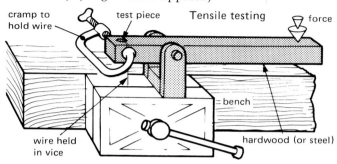

FORMULAS

$$\text{Tensile strength (stress)} = \frac{\text{force (N)}}{\text{cross-sectional area (mm}^2)}$$

$$\text{Strain} = \frac{\text{final length} - \text{original length}}{\text{original length}} \times 100\%$$

Compression testing

The same device as that used for tensile testing can be used by rearranging it as shown below. Use short test pieces for compression testing, otherwise they buckle. Only weaker materials can be tested with this equipment (e.g. wood, plaster, concrete).

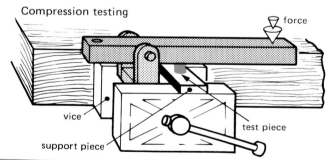

The effect of heat

Put a drop of wax on one end of the test pieces, then heat the other end. Record if the wax melted and if the material burned. (*Safety* Hold work in tongs.)

Corrosion resistance

To speed up the effect of corrosion taking place, put one set of your test pieces in an acid (e.g. vinegar) and the other set in a moist alkaline (e.g. salty water) environment. Then leave them for a few weeks before recording results. (*Note* Half of each test piece should be in the air.)

Electrical conductivity

Test for this by using a simple circuit consisting of a bulb, battery and wires. If the bulb lights up the material is a **conductor**; if it does not it is an **insulator**.

METALS AND THEIR PROPERTIES

The most common metals and ways of altering their properties are described here. Metals are made from **ores** which are mined from the earth. The most common metals are steel and aluminium. **Steel** is made from **iron ore** and **aluminium** from an **ore** called **bauxite**.

MAKING STEEL

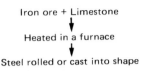

Iron ore + Limestone
↓
Heated in a furnace
↓
Steel rolled or cast into shape

Alloys

Metals that are mixed together during manufacture are called **alloys**. For example, pure aluminium is weak, but when alloyed it is strong enough to be used in aircraft construction.

Ferrous and non-ferrous metals

Metals naturally divide up into two main groups: those **containing iron** are called **ferrous** and those **without iron** are called **non-ferrous**.

1 FERROUS METALS (metals with iron)

Cast iron and steel are two ferrous metals. The main problem with ferrous metals is that they are prone to **rust**: They therefore need some form of 'surface protection', such as paint.

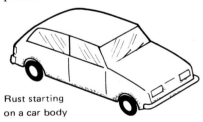

Rust starting
on a car body

Cast iron

Cast iron contains 2–4% carbon. It is hard, brittle reasonably cheap and is usually **cast** into intricate shapes, such as car cylinder blocks for engines and drain covers. It is rarely used in schools as a construction material.

Steels

Steels are classified by the amount of carbon they contain; they are divided into three main types.

1 Mild steel is the most common type of steel. It contains 0.1–0.3% carbon. It is a general purpose steel which is reasonably strong and easy to form. It can be joined by brazing, welding and soldering. The 'low carbon' content means that it **cannot** be hardened by heat treatment.

Steel screw for wood   Paper punch

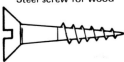
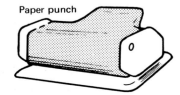

2 Medium carbon steel contains 0.3–0.7% carbon. It is stronger and harder than mild steel and is used for hammer heads and wire ropes etc.

3 High carbon steel contain 0.7–1.4% carbon. It is the hardest steel but can be made even harder by heat treatment. This makes it especially good for cutting tools such as metalwork files, lathe cutting tools and thread cutting tools etc.

Note Steels with 1–1.4% carbon are sometimes called tool steels.

Cold chisel   Screwdriver blade

Stainless steel

This special steel is made stainless by alloying steel and corrosion-resisting metals such as chromium and nickel. It is a hard, tough material used to make stainless steel knives, kettles etc.

ANNEALING

When steel is 'worked' (e.g. hammered) it becomes harder; annealing is used to soften the metal again.
Steel Heat to bright red heat, leave it to 'soak' in the heat for a few minutes, then let it cool very slowly.

HARDENING AND TEMPERING STEEL

Hardening. **High carbon steel** can be **hardened** by heating to a **bright red** heat, then **quenching** it in water. The steel is now too hard and brittle for practical use, so some of the hardness is removed by **tempering**. The amount of hardness removed by tempering will depend on what the high carbon steel is to be used for.

Tempering consists of reheating the steel to the tempering temperature and then quenching it again. The temperature at which the steel has to be quenched can be judged by watching the **tempering colours** on the metal (see **tempering chart** below). Before tempering, 'clean' the steel with 'emery cloth' so that the tempering colours can be seen. Allow the tempering colours to 'flow' to the working part when heating with a gas/air torch.

Tempering colours
move to end

HEAT

Screwdriver blade being tempered

Steel tempering chart (oxide colours)

	Colour	Use
	Blue	for springs, screwdrivers, spanners
	Purple	for cold chisels, hacksaw blades
	Red/Brown	for hammer heads, drills
	Dark yellow	punches, knives, taps and dies
	Light yellow	scribers, dividers, lathe tools

2 NON-FERROUS METALS (without iron)

Aluminium

Aluminium is light, has a low melting temperature for a metal, 650–670°C. It is a good conductor of heat and electricity, can be polished easily (e.g. on a polishing machine), but it is difficult to join using hot joining methods because of the **oxides** produced on its surface. It is used for aircraft construction, pistons, window frames etc.

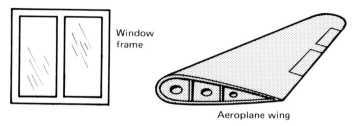

Window frame

Aeroplane wing

Copper

Copper is a very good conductor of electricity and can easily be worked into a bowl shape. It is a heavy metal, easy to solder and braze, but it is rather expensive. It is used for electric wires, vases, waterpipes etc.

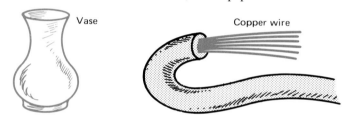

Vase

Copper wire

Brass

Brass is a yellow alloy made from 60% copper and 40% zinc. It is a fairly hard, brittle metal, it machines and solders quite well, and is used for screws and electrical parts etc.

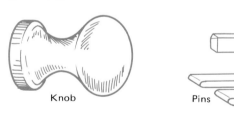

Knob

Pins

Lead

Lead is a very heavy metal with a low melting temperature. It should not be used in school workshops because it is poisonous and can cause brain damage.

Solder made from a lead and tin alloy

MULTICORE
SOFT
SOLDER
TIN/LEAD

Zinc

Zinc is not normally used by itself but is often found as a coating on steel to prevent it rusting; this is called **galvanising.**

Chromium

Chromium is a valuable alloying metal. It is also used to produce **chromed** shiny, easy-to-clean surfaces; for example bath taps, nail clippers, cutlery etc.

Fork

Nail clippers

Silver and gold

Both are anti-corrosive, have good electrical conductivity, and are expensive. They are used to make expensive jewellery and in the micro-electronics industry because of their good electrical properties.

Silver pendant

Gold ring

ANNEALING NON-FERROUS METALS

When metals are worked (e.g. hammered) they harden. Annealing can soften the metal again, making it easier to shape and form. Different metals require different techniques to anneal them:

Aluminium. Rub it with **soap**, then heat it until the **soap turns black** (this indicates the correct temperature). Then leave it to cool.

Copper. Heat it to **cherry red** heat, then **quench** it in water.

Brass (and gilding metal). Heat to a **dull red**, then leave it to cool.

Question

What metals do you think the following metal objects would be made from?

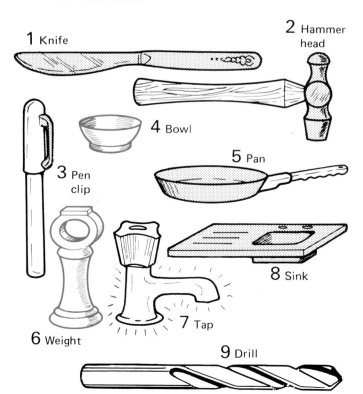

1 Knife

2 Hammer head

3 Pen clip

4 Bowl

5 Pan

6 Weight

7 Tap

8 Sink

9 Drill

PLASTICS AND THEIR PROPERTIES

The plastics story only really began about 110 years ago. It would now be hard to imagine life without plastic products such as: felt-tip pens, carpets, tiles, plastic bottles, bowls, tights, toys, toothbrushes, baths, etc. Plastics, unlike wood or metals, are manufactured in chemical plants.

Plastics are made from long **chains of molecules** called **polymers**:

A great variety of materials are used to make plastics. The first plastics were made from easy-to-find materials such as plants and insects. From these were produced the early plastic varnishes such as shellac, and french polish. Nowadays plastics are usually manufactured from crude oil, coal and gases.

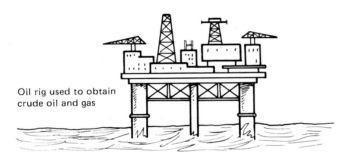

Oil rig used to obtain crude oil and gas

Advantages of plastics

- They are easy to form by moulding, casting and cutting using ordinary workshop tools.
- No surface protection is needed.
- They have good chemical and weather resistance.
- They can be supplied in sheet form, as a resin, as granules, as foams, etc.
- A wide range of colours and textures are available.

Disadvantages of plastics

- Some have a rather narrow temperature range in which they can be used, e.g. acrylic is brittle below 0°C but is soft and leather like at 160°C.
- Some plastics are a fire risk.
- Some plastics become brittle with age and in sunlight.

Types of plastics

There are three main types of plastics (or polymers): **thermoplastics**, **thermosets** and **elastomers**.

Thermoplastics

These are made from long molecules which are free to slide about when heat and force are applied.

Thermoplastics form the largest grouping. These plastics soften when heated and harden again at room temperature. On being heated, the long polymer chains slide over one another, allowing the material to be moulded easily. Thermoplastics can easily be moulded after heating up on a 'strip heater' or in an oven.

EXAMPLES OF THERMOPLASTICS

Acrylic (perspex) A commonly used plastic in school, it is supplied in sheets of various colours and textures. It is a hard, rigid plastic which can be moulded at 160°C. It is often used as a glass substitute and for products that need to have a good shiny finish; for example shop signs, shop fittings, baths and plastic lenses etc.

Photo display

Keyfob

S.D.

PVC (poly-vinyl-chloride) It is a reasonably cheap plastic which can either be supplied as a rigid sheet or as a soft flexible roll (if a plasticiser has been added). It is easy to mould and cut and is used for drainpipes, hosepipes, records, car seat covers and raincoats.

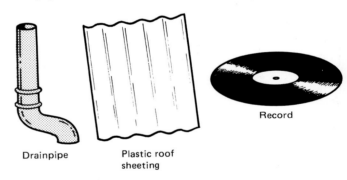

Drainpipe

Plastic roof sheeting

Record

Nylon This is a very tough plastic, often used for zips, gearwheels, hinges, door catches, and as a yarn it is used for clothing. Nylon does not glue easily. Solid bar shapes can be 'turned down' easily on the lathe.

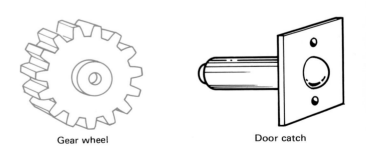

Gear wheel

Door catch

Polystyrene comes in two main forms: (i) as a foamed plastic (e.g. ceiling tiles), or (ii) as a normal solid plastic bought in sheet form etc. Solid sheet vacuum-forms very well, softening at about 90°C. It is used for products such as: children's modelling kits, food containers and packaging. Polystyrene glue produces very strong joints on solid polystyrene. *Note* **Do not** use polystyrene glues on expanded polystyrene because it dissolves the foam.

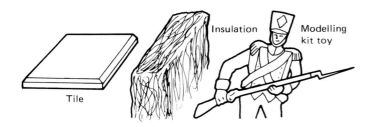

Tile   Insulation   Modelling kit toy

Polythene (polyethene) Polythene is sold as 'low density polythene' or 'high density polythene'. It is very tough and flexible but is hard to glue. It is used for polythene bags, bowls and containers.

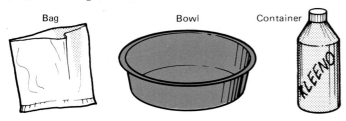

Bag   Bowl   Container

Polypropylene Polypropylene is a tough, lighter-than-water plastic which welds easily. It will not break when flexed. It is used for hinges, ropes, large food containers etc.

Container with integral hinge   Rope

PTFE (poly-tetra-fluoro-ethylene) This is the non-stick frying pan plastic, used because of its low friction properties. It is rather expensive.

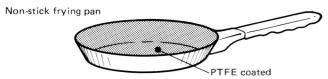

Non-stick frying pan   PTFE coated

Thermosets

Once made, these plastics cannot be softened by heating, because the polymers have **'cross-linked'** together. This property makes them useful for electric light fittings which must not be softened due to the heat of the bulb.

The molecules are CROSS LINKED

THERMOSET EXAMPLES

Polyester resin is rather like treacle (resin) but when mixed with a **hardener** it sets hard and brittle. It is often reinforced with glass fibres to make **glass reinforced plastic** (GRP). Products that are made in this way include canoes and some car bodies. A special thin clear polyester resin can be used for embedding objects. *Note* Keep **resin** and **hardener** apart until needed because they can react violently.

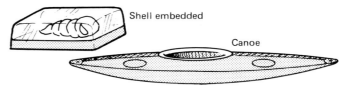

Shell embedded   Canoe

Epoxy resin This is similar to polyester resin but has more stable properties. It is used for glues and car repair kits.

Epoxy adhesive   Repair kit

Urea-formaldehyde A hard brittle plastic, it is used to make electric light fittings and kitchen worktop surfaces the different patterns available are produced by laminating with patterned paper.

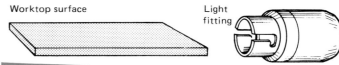

Worktop surface   Light fitting

Elastomers

This is the rubbers group. Some people do not consider rubbers as plastics but they are included because they are polymers. Elastomers are very flexible and elastic. Rubbers are used for tyres, elastic bands, oil seals, roller skate wheels etc.

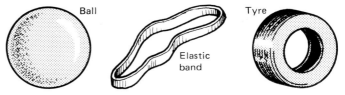

Ball   Elastic band   Tyre

ADDITIVES TO PLASTICS

The properties of plastics can be altered by adding **fillers** and **plasticisers**.

Fillers are powders added for various reasons, e.g. chalk can be added to polyester resin to make it go further and reduce its brittleness.

Plasticisers are added to make some of the rigid plastics more flexible, e.g. plasticised PVC is used to produce a leather effect.

Question

What plastics do you think have been used to make the following products?

Tube (large dia.)   Cup   Record   Magnifier   Bucket   Sole

WOOD AND ITS PROPERTIES

Wood comes from **felled** trees which are then transported and **converted** in the sawmills into thick plank sizes. The wood is then **seasoned**, cut into the sizes required and dried outside or in a special kiln. This reduces the moisture content to about 10% for indoor work and about 18% for outdoor work.

Seasoning wood outside

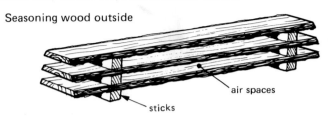

air spaces

sticks

Advantages of wood

- Wood is easy to work (using common cutting tools).
- It glues easily.
- It is warm to the touch.
- It has an attractive appearance.
- It is easy to obtain.
- It is reasonably cheap.
- Wood is electric and heat insulating.

Disadvantages

- Protection is usually needed against insect and fungal attack.
- It can warp and shrink as it dries.
- Wood easily splits along the grain.
- It cannot be cast like metal.
- Its size is limited by the tree size (but processed boards overcome this problem).

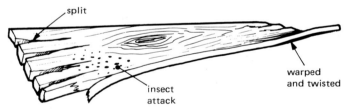

split

insect attack

warped and twisted

HOW A TREE GROWS

Trees need **water** and **mineral salts**, taken in by the roots. In **sap** they rise up the tree where the action of the **sunlight** on the **chlorophyll** (the green matter of leaves) combines the water with **carbon dioxide** from the air to produce new growth.

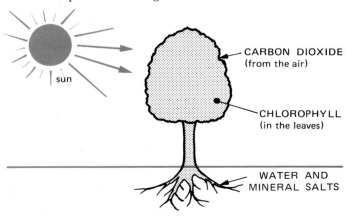

sun

CARBON DIOXIDE (from the air)

CHLOROPHYLL (in the leaves)

WATER AND MINERAL SALTS

When a tree is felled the growth can be seen as **annual rings**. Most of the trunk is **sapwood** which is living and growing, but as time goes on the centre part stops growing and hardens to form the **heartwood**. Most growth activity takes place in the **cambium layer** which is just beneath the **bark**.

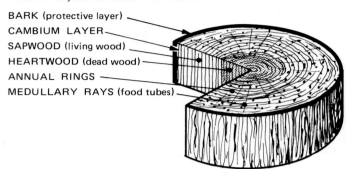

BARK (protective layer)
CAMBIUM LAYER
SAPWOOD (living wood)
HEARTWOOD (dead wood)
ANNUAL RINGS
MEDULLARY RAYS (food tubes)

Softwoods and hardwoods

SOFTWOODS

Softwoods come from **conifer** trees. They are generally softer than hardwoods, hence their name. The wood is commonly called **pine** in the shops. The building trade uses softwoods for most of its construction work because of its cheapness and availability.

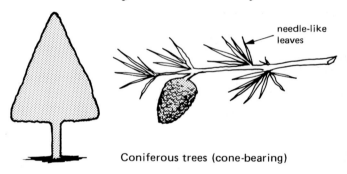

needle-like leaves

Coniferous trees (cone-bearing)

Some softwoods
Scots pine (brown or yellowish) It is used for joinery work.
Cedar (reddish brown) A very useful outdoor wood, e.g. for cedar greenhouses, window frames. It is a fairly soft wood.
Spruce (white to yellowish brown) It is used for construction work, oars and gliders etc. It is strong for its weight.
Yew (orange to dark brown) It is fairly expensive and is used for veneers and wood turning.

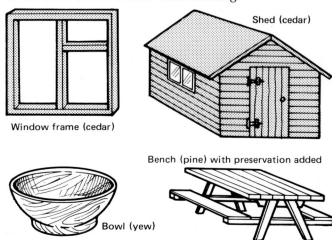

Shed (cedar)

Window frame (cedar)

Bench (pine) with preservation added

Bowl (yew)

HARDWOODS

Hardwoods come from **deciduous** trees (most of which are hard, hence the name of this group). Deciduous trees have broad leaves which are 'shed' in the winter. There is a great range of hardwoods, from the quite soft 'hardwoods', e.g. balsa wood, to the very hard hardwoods such as ebony.

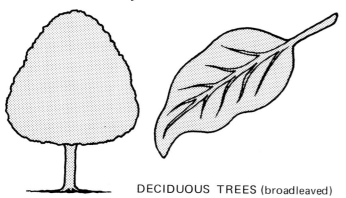

DECIDUOUS TREES (broadleaved)

Some hardwoods

Oak (light brown) A very hard wood, often used for furniture and decorative veneers and general high quality work. (Steel screws rust in oak; brass screws must be used instead.)

Beech (light brown or pinkish) A tough close-grained wood making it suitable for tool handles, unpainted toys, rolling pins, furniture and work benches.

Ash (whitish) A hard tough wood used for sports equipment, handles and internal joinery.

Mahogany (reddish brown) It is used a great deal for veneers on chipboard. A very decorative wood used for high-class furniture. (Many varieties of mahogany are available.)

Teak (light brown) It is used for high-class furniture, tables, boats etc. It is resistant to decay.

Balsa (white) Although it is very soft, it is in fact still in the hardwood category because it is a deciduous wood. It is used for model making.

Obeche Light coloured and soft to work.

PROCESSED WOOD

Processed wood overcomes some of the disadvantages of 'real' wood. It comes in large sheets that do not shrink or warp, often with the final surface finish added during manufacture, e.g. varnish, paint, wood or plastic laminates etc. Examples include:

Hardboard, made from pulped wood and glue which is then compressed. One side is smooth, the other rough. (Cheap.)

Chipboard, made from wood chips glued together. It is often laminated with wood or plastic.

Blockboard, made from glued strips of wood covered with veneer (thin sheets of wood).

Plywood, consisting of layers of wood veneer glued together at 90 degrees to each other. Marine ply is a plywood that can be used outdoors.

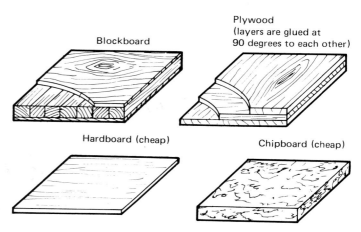

Blockboard

Plywood (layers are glued at 90 degrees to each other)

Hardboard (cheap)

Chipboard (cheap)

Question

What woods do you think have been used to produce the following?

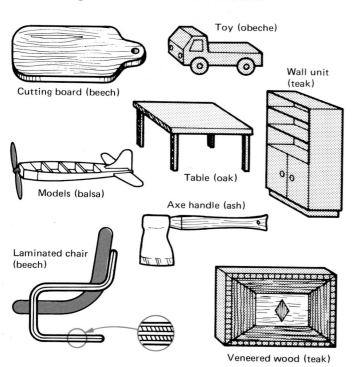

Cutting board (beech)

Toy (obeche)

Wall unit (teak)

Models (balsa)

Table (oak)

Axe handle (ash)

Laminated chair (beech)

Veneered wood (teak)

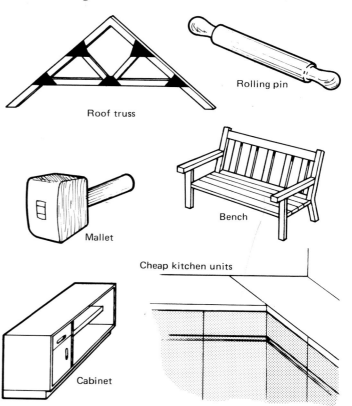

Roof truss

Rolling pin

Mallet

Bench

Cheap kitchen units

Cabinet

SHAPING AND FORMING MATERIALS

The shaping and forming of materials is covered under the following headings:

1 **Marking out** (page 54)
2 **Shaping by cutting** (pages 55–56)
3 **Shaping by moulding** (pages 57–59)
4 **Shaping by casting** (pages 60–61)
5 **Fabrication techniques,** including adhesives (pages 62–64)
6 **Obtaining a good finish** (page 65)

There then follow some **Exercises** covering this section.

1 MARKING OUT

Tools commonly used

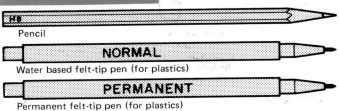

Pencil

NORMAL
Water based felt-tip pen (for plastics)

PERMANENT
Permanent felt-tip pen (for plastics)

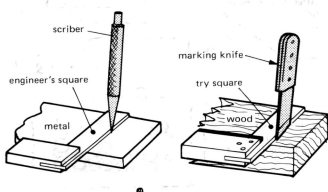

scriber
engineer's square
metal
marking knife
try square
wood

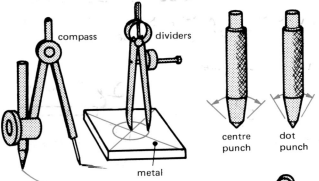

compass
dividers
centre punch
dot punch
metal

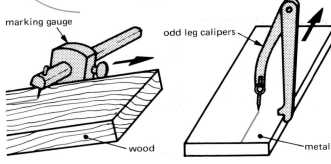

marking gauge
odd leg calipers
wood
metal

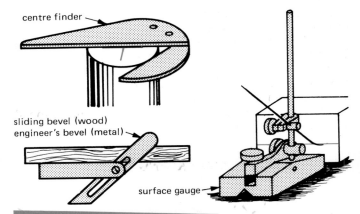

centre finder
sliding bevel (wood)
engineer's bevel (metal)
surface gauge

Three marking-out methods

The three methods shown below involve marking out: from a **CENTRE LINE**, from a **TRUE EDGE**, and using a **TEMPLATE**.
Note Always avoid waste, mark out from a corner if possible.

1 MARKING OUT FROM A CENTRE LINE
(useful for symmetrical shapes, as shown)

(a) centre line
(b) waste

2 STAGES IN MARKING OUT FROM A TRUE EDGE

(a) Test edge is true.
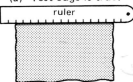
ruler

(b) Square both ends.
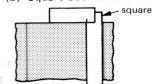
square

(c) Mark off width.
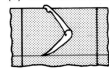

(d) Mark out hole centre if required.
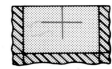

(e) Centre punch centre (metal)
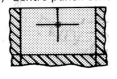

(f) Cut out the **waste** side of the line, then true up all edges.

3 MARKING OUT USING A TEMPLATE

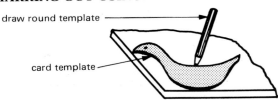

draw round template
card template

54

2 SHAPING BY CUTTING

This is probably the most common method of shaping and forming in schools. This page illustrates tools and processes used to cut metals and plastics. Most of the next page illustrates tools and processes used to cut wood. One of the main reasons for producing a shape by cutting is that the final shape can be made very accurately. One of the problems with cutting is that there is often a lot of waste (e.g. wood shavings etc.). Your school may be lucky enough to have some power tools, which make a lot of the traditional 'hand tools' seem like hard work.

NOTES ON SAWS AND SAWING

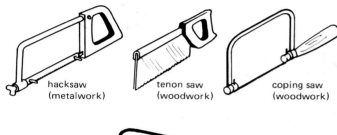

hacksaw (metalwork)   tenon saw (woodwork)   coping saw (woodwork)

Three or more teeth needed on the work when cutting.

always cut on the *waste side of the line.*

Abrafiles are rather delicate round file-like blades that fit in hacksaw and are used to cut thin materials.

NOTES ON FILES AND FILING

Parts of a file

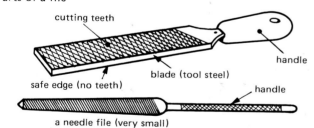

cutting teeth

handle

safe edge (no teeth)   blade (tool steel)

handle

a needle file (very small)

Cross-cut filing (for roughing out)

Draw filing (for finishing off)

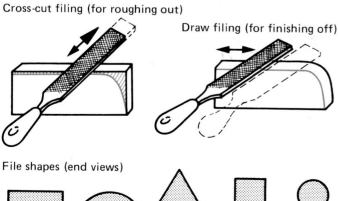

File shapes (end views)

flat   half round   triangular   square   round

SHEARS (or tinsnips)

They are used like scissors to cut thin metal etc.

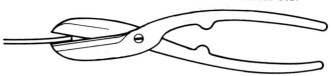

NOTES ON CUTTING OUT HOLES WITH DRILLS

Common hole cutter

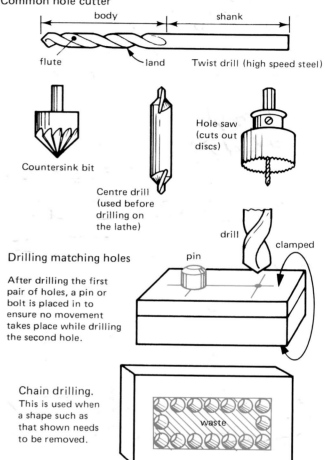

body   shank

flute   land   Twist drill (high speed steel)

Countersink bit

Centre drill (used before drilling on the lathe)

Hole saw (cuts out discs)

Drilling matching holes

After drilling the first pair of holes, a pin or bolt is placed in to ensure no movement takes place while drilling the second hole.

pin   drill   clamped

Chain drilling. This is used when a shape such as that shown needs to be removed.

waste

STAGES IN THREADING AN EXTERNAL AND AN INTERNAL THREAD (6 mm in diameter)

Cutting an external thread

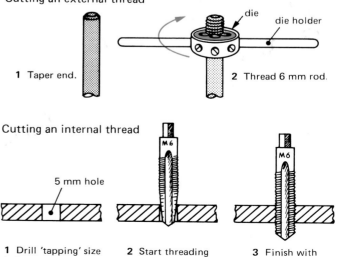

die   die holder

1 Taper end.   **2** Thread 6 mm rod.

Cutting an internal thread

5 mm hole

M6   M6

1 Drill 'tapping' size hole.   **2** Start threading with a 'taper tap'.   **3** Finish with the 'plug tap'.

Woodwork cutting tools

PLANES

Planes are used for cutting wood and some plastics. They consist of a sharp blade which cuts thin shavings from the wood. Various plane types are shown below.

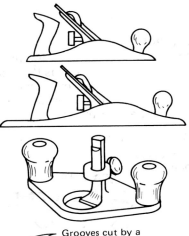

A Smoothing plane – A general-purpose plane for flat surfaces

B Jack plane – Used for longer more accurate work

C Router plane – Cleans up housing joints after much of the wood has been cut by sawing and chiselling

D Plough plane (not drawn). This special plane has a thin blade that can cut grooves along the grain as shown.

Grooves cut by a plough plane

Question: What plane types were used to produce this?

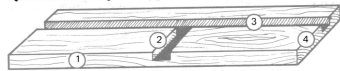

Answers: 1, **A** or **B**. 2, **C**. 3, **D**. 4, **A**.

CHISELS AND GOUGES

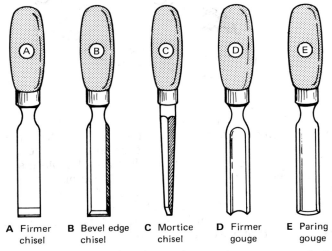

A Firmer chisel **B** Bevel edge chisel **C** Mortice chisel **D** Firmer gouge **E** Paring gouge

Question: What chisels and gouges were used to produce this?

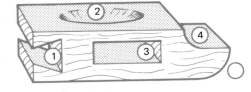

Answers: 1, **B**. 2, **D**. 3, **C**. 4, **E**. 5, **A**.

WOODBORING TOOLS

Bradawl — Produces a 'pilot hole' for screws

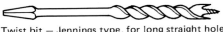

Twist bit — Jennings type, for long straight holes

Flat bit — Used in electric power drills

Expansive bit — An adjustable bit

RASPS

The traditional rasp

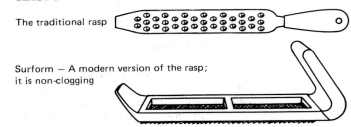

Surform — A modern version of the rasp; it is non-clogging

LATHE WORK

Examples of shapes turned on a **wood** lathe

Examples of shapes turned on a **metal** lathe

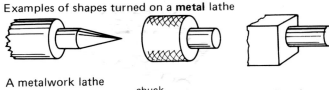

A metalwork lathe

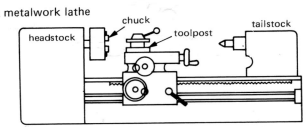

headstock chuck toolpost tailstock

Exercises

1 Make a list of all the cutting and marking-out tools you can think of, then indicate with a (W), (M) or (P) which are suitable for use with Wood, Metal and Plastics.

2 Explain how you would 'mark out' a rectangular hole 40 mm × 20 mm in the centre of a 80 mm × 60 mm piece of (a) wood, (b) metal and (c) plastic (thickness is 4 mm).

Note You must indicate which tools you use either in note form or as drawings.

3 SHAPING BY MOULDING

Moulding is a general term used to describe the **shaping and forming of materials using force**. The force applied can be by: the use of finger pressure, the use of a hammer, the use of clamps etc. A material that moulds very easily is clay. A material that requires a lot of force to mould it is steel. Steel is heated to red heat to make it easier to mould into shape.

All materials can be moulded but some are much easier to mould than others. Wood is one of the more difficult materials to mould, but most plastics are easy to mould, and soften when a little heat is applied.

Moulding wood

Thick pieces of wood are difficult to bend into shape. One way to mould wood which overcomes this problem is called **laminating**. Thin layers of wood, called **veneers** which bend easily are glued together in a mould (sometimes called a former) and left to set. The shapes produced in this way are extremely strong because the wood's grain follows the form produced.

STAGES IN LAMINATING A SALAD SERVER

(a) Select or make the mould to be used. Protect the parts that may be covered in glue with polythene.
(b) Glue the layers of thin wood (veneers) together, see diagrams below. (Use a waterproof glue for a salad server because it will need washing.)
(c) Place glued veneers in the mould and clamp it up carefully.
(d) When the glue has set, remove the work from the mould.
(e) 'Mark out' the salad server shape on the laminated wood, using a card template.
(f) Cut out shape.

(a) + (b)

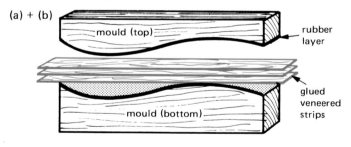

(c)

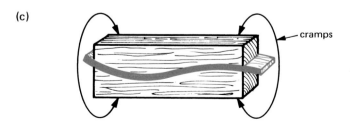

(d) + (e)

Salad servers made by laminating

Moulding metals

Some metals can be moulded reasonably easily. They are the **ductile** metals such as copper, aluminium, silver and gold. They can be bent or beaten into shape in their cold state. Steels which are tougher are often moulded hot; this is called **forging.** Below are various methods of moulding metals.

SIMPLE BENDS

Simple bends can be made in the vice or in special **jigs** as shown. If the metal is thin enough it may be possible to bend it by hand or with the help of a hammer. You may have seen a more sophisticated jig used to bend copper heating pipes (sometimes called a pipe bender).

Simple bending jig
(Pins can be moved to different holes)

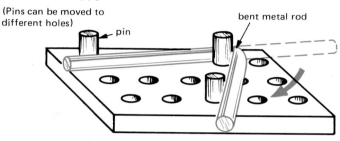

BENDING THIN SHEET METAL

To bend sheet metal accurately, hold the metal between two strong metal strips as shown below. Sometimes a vice or special folding bars can be used to hold the work. Bend the metal over using a heavy mallet. To avoid denting the metal, use a strip of wood.

Bending sheet metal

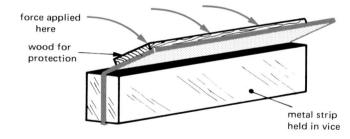

BEATEN METAL

This is the method used to hand-produce compound curves such as a bowl or vase. (In industry such shapes are usually 'press moulded' or 'stamped out' in one go.)

To make a bowl in school, select a malleable metal like copper and anneal it (see page 49). Using a bossing mallet and a wooden mould, start round the outer edge, working towards the centre, at the same time turning the bowl. Anneal again if necessary. (A sandbag can be used instead of a wooden mould.)

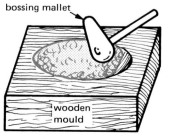

Start of bowl

Finished bowl

Moulding metals (continued)

FORGEWORK
Forging makes use of the fact that red hot steel is easier to bend and mould than cold steel. Aim to keep the part that is to be forged 'red hot'. If it is white hot the steel will be ruined, if too cold the steel may crack. Three common forging operations are shown below.

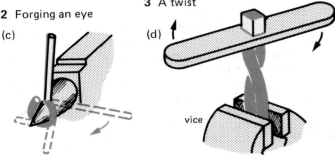

1 Drawing down a point
(a)
anvil
(b)

2 Forging an eye
(c)

3 A twist
(d)
vice

Moulding plastics

Plastics are ideally suited to moulding because they are easily softened with heat. The force required to mould plastics is much less than for metal.

All the moulding methods described below can easily be carried out in schools. However, injection moulding machines are expensive.

USING A STRIP HEATER
A strip heater is used a great deal in schools for moulding sheet plastic. It consists of an electric element that glows red hot. In order to prevent the plastic sheet being burnt it must be turned over every 10 seconds or so. When the plastic has softened it easily bends with a little hand pressure.

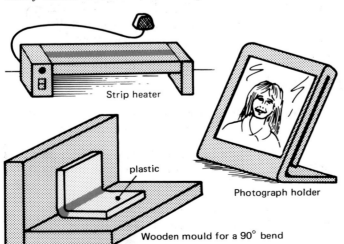

Strip heater

plastic

Photograph holder

Wooden mould for a 90° bend

PLASTIC MEMORY MOULDING
If you heat a thick **thermoplastic** (e.g. acrylic) and compress part of it, then reheat it, the plastic will return to its original form (i.e. it 'remembers' its original form). We can use this idea to make relief patterns etc. The example below shows how an O-shape is made using this memory technique.

(a) Select a metal ring without sharp edges.
(b) Heat the plastic until soft, then push the metal ring into the plastic.
(c) When cool, remove the ring, then file away the plastic groove made.
(d) Reheat it and a plastic ring appears as if by magic.

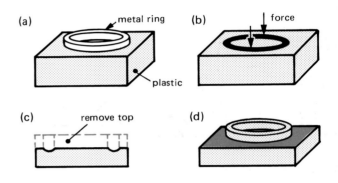

(a) metal ring, plastic
(b) force
(c) remove top
(d)

VACUUM FORMING
Vacuum forming is used to make: plastic trays, fridge liners, acrylic sinks and baths etc. The small vacuum forming machines used in schools will be capable of forming only thin sheets of plastic such as PVC and polystyrene over a mould. These are the stages in vacuum forming:

(a) Clamp a plastic sheet in the machine, then heat it until it is soft and pliable.
(b) Pump the air out quickly (using the vacuum pump) and the plastic sheet will then be forced onto the mould by the air pressure above it. When the moulded plastic sheet is cool, it can be removed.

Vacuum forming — shown in section

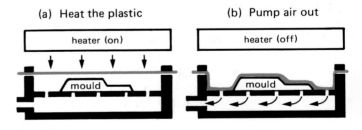

(a) Heat the plastic
heater (on)
mould

(b) Pump air out
heater (off)
mould

Car shape vacuum formed (note rounded corners)

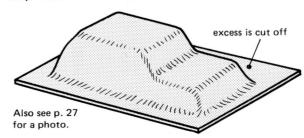

excess is cut off

Also see p. 27 for a photo.

PRESS MOULDING

This method of forming can produce forms similar to those obtained by vacuum forming, but it has the advantage that thicker plastic can be moulded.

Stages in press moulding an acrylic soap dish

- Heat acrylic sheet in oven at 160°C.
- Using leather gloves, place the hot plastic over the mould.
- Hold the top ring in place (if needed).
- Push the 'plug' down into the mould.

Note Speed is essential to avoid the plastic cooling too soon.

Press moulding

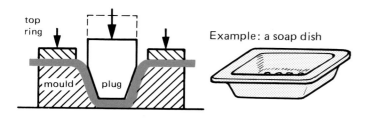

Example: a soap dish

BLOW MOULDING

Sheet plastic can be blow moulded either freely into the air (as shown) or into a mould. A dome can be made as follows:

- Clamp the plastic sheet in the jig.
- Heat plastic until it has softened (an electric heater can be used, or the whole lot can be placed in an oven).
- Air is pumped into the jig to inflate the plastic dome.

Blow moulding a dome

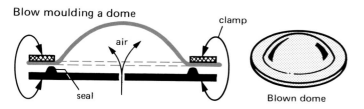

Blown dome

INJECTION MOULDING

Injection moulding is a mass production method used to produce buckets, radio cases, control knobs, toys etc.

This is how plastic buckets are made:
- Plastic pellets are heated in the heating chamber.
- The piston or a screw feeder forces the hot plastic into moulds.
- When cool enough, the plastic moulding is removed by opening up the mould.
- The **sprue** is then cut off.

Injection moulding a bucket

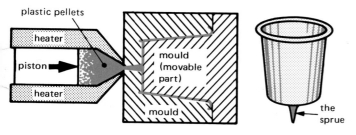

GLASS REINFORCED PLASTICS (GRP)

Glass fibres which by themselves are very strong are embedded in cold setting resin (e.g. polyester resin or epoxy resin) to produce a material that is stronger than steel, weight for weight, is easy (but messy) to use, and is resistant to most chemicals. Glass reinforced plastics (GRPs) are used to make boats, signs, 'car kit' bodies etc. Polyester resin is the plastic most commonly used; it sets in 10 to 20 minutes depending on the amount of **hardener** added, temperature and thickness.

STEPS IN 'LAYING UP' A MOULD

Make sure you work in a well ventilated area and you have protected the benches and yourself from spills. Ask your teacher to mix the resins for you.

(a) Prepare the mould by waxing the mould surface three times (wood will need varnishing first).
(b) Apply the **gel-coat** (which is an extra-thick resin) with a brush; colour can be added with the hardener.
(c) Wait until the gel-coat has set.
(d) The layers of reinforcing glassfibres can now be added by **stippling** on with a brush using **lay up resin**, which is thinner than gel-coat. Once the first layer is stippled on, continue without waiting for the first layer to set.
(e) The last layer can be made reasonably smooth by using a fine glassfibre called **surface tissue**.
(f) Trim the edges using wood tools, or metalwork tools at the **'green'** stage.
(g) Remove from the mould when the resin has set hard.

Steps in 'laying up' GRP

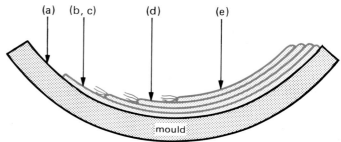

Canoe moulded in GRP

Exercises

1 Explain the steps required to make your initials in acrylic using the 'plastic memory moulding' technique.
2 Explain the steps required to make a salad server using three layers of wood veneer (assume a suitable mould is available).
3 Explain the steps required to make a photograph holder similar to that shown on page 58.
4 Explain the steps required to make a fruit dish by press moulding.

4 SHAPING BY CASTING

Casting here refers to the pouring of a liquid material into a mould where it 'sets'. No force is used to cast; the material flows freely in and around the mould. Some people think of casting as meaning only metal casting, such as car or motorcycle engine cylinder blocks, vice castings, bronze sculptures etc., but plastics, concrete, plaster of paris and wax are also cast to make jewellery, decorative wall blocks, cast animals, candles etc. Various casting methods are described below.

CASTING A FIGURE IN PLASTER OF PARIS
– using a rubber mould

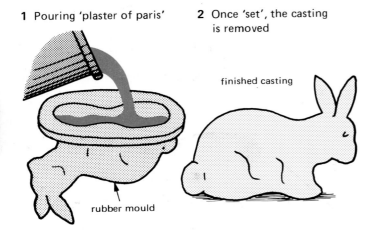

1 Pouring 'plaster of paris'

2 Once 'set', the casting is removed

finished casting

rubber mould

PLASTIC RESIN CASTING
This is similar to plaster of paris casting except that the end result is much stronger. To make chess pieces you need rubber moulds and a plastic resin (usually polyester resin).

- Make a card support for the mould.
- Mix resin, catalyst (hardener) and colour.
- Half-fill the mould and squeeze any trapped bubbles out.
- Fill the mould up to the 'shoulder'.
- When the resin has set (in 30–40 minutes), remove rubber mould and trim the base.

Note A If the resin overheats, put it in cold water.
Note B Powdered chalk or other fillers can be added to the resin to make the castings cheaper and less likely to crack.

pouring in resin mix into the rubber mould

rubber mould

Finished casting

Castle chess piece cast in polyster resin and finished

EMBEDDING
Hard objects such as coins, shells and electronic parts can be embedded (or encapsulated) in **clear casting polyester resins**. Embedding is used to make decorative items such as paperweights, or to protect delicate objects.

Stages in embedding a shell
(a) Mix and pour the first layer of clear casting resin in the mould. Only a little resin needs to be mixed for this.
(b) When the first layer has set, place the object to be embedded in position.
(c) Mix some fresh clear casting resin and pour it over the shell until covered.
(d) A coloured layer of resin can be added for the base.
(e) Remove casting from the mould and either glue a piece of felt on its base or clean it up with 'wet and dry' emery paper.

Note If the layers are too thick or if too much hardener has been added, the casting may heat up and crack.

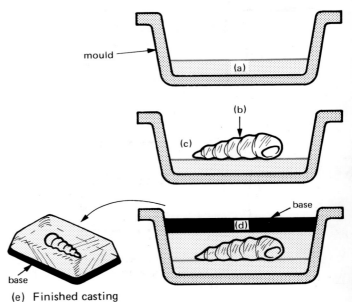

mould

base

base

(e) Finished casting

CASTING THERMOPLASTICS
Plastic powders (e.g. nylon) can be melted in metal moulds. This method can be used to make very tough castings.

To make wheels
Fill the metal mould with powder and place it in an oven. When the plastic has melted remove it from the oven to cool.
Note The powder settles down as shown when heated.

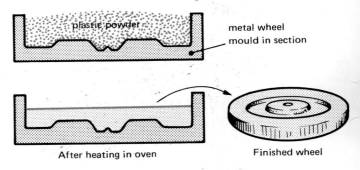

plastic powder

metal wheel mould in section

After heating in oven

Finished wheel

CASTING METALS

In schools the casting of metals is limited to easy-to-melt metals such as aluminium.

Metal casting can be dangerous. Teacher supervision is needed.

Stages in casting a lamp stand base

1 Place pattern in bottom half of the moulding box (**drag**) and then ram 'moulding sand' down on top of the pattern.

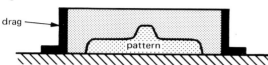

2 Carefully turn the **drag** upside down as shown. Shake **parting sand** over the surface, then place the top box (**cope**) on. Fill and ram the **cope** with sand, at the same time holding the tapered **sprue pins** in place.

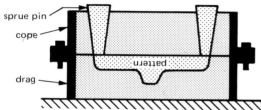

3 Carefully remove the sprue pins and the pattern from the moulding sand, then pour the metal in via the runner.

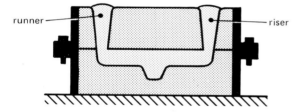

4 When the cast metal has cooled the mould can be broken open to reveal the casting. The extra **runner** and **riser** pieces are cut off.

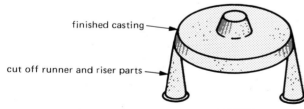

A table lamp made using an aluminium casting for its base

Notes
The casting has tapered sides and rounded edges. The surface finish is not very smooth because the metal was cast into a sand mould.

Enamelling

There are two main ways of enamelling:

Hot enamelling uses powdered glass which is melted on a piece of copper.
Cold cast enamelling uses 'cold enamelling resins'. This can be used on various surfaces including cardboard. The method described below is hot enamelling. It is the most popular but it has the disadvantage that the enamel used is brittle and will crack if bent.

Stages in enamelling a pendant

- Cut out the shape from a piece of copper, round off the edges and clean the surfaces in acid or with emery cloth. (Any holes must be drilled at this stage.)
- Paint the copper blank with a thin layer of glue (e.g. wallpaper paste) to hold the enamel powder in place and to prevent scales forming.
- Sieve enamel powder onto the copper. Do this on a large sheet of paper to catch the excess which can be re-used (see below).

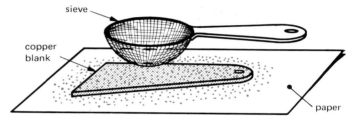

- Place on a support (e.g. wire mesh) and heat it in an enamelling kiln, or with a brazing torch, until the glass powder melts and fuses together.
- Let it cool slowly (about 3 minutes) to avoid enamel cracking.
- Add any extra decoration you want (see below for ideas). Then heat again.
- Place pendant in the acid bath to remove the oxides from the copper (or use emery cloth).

Decoration ideas for enamelling

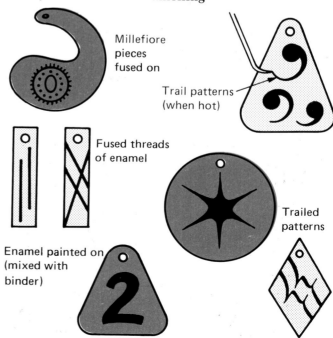

5 FABRICATION TECHNIQUES

Joining methods

When fabricating (assembling) your work it is important that you choose the best methods. Materials are joined in one of **three** ways to produce –

- **permanent joints,** or
- **temporary joints** (joints that can be undone easily such as bolts), or
- **movable joints** (joints that allow movement such as a hinge).

The next three pages describe a few of the possible joining methods you are likely to meet.

Permanent joints

ADHESIVES
One of the easiest methods of joining is to glue the parts together. To ensure you obtain a strong joint,

- select the most appropriate glue (see below for selection).
- glue as large a surface area as possible.
- make sure the joint is clean and dry.
- roughen any shiny surfaces before gluing.
- clamp joints if possible.

Note Some materials are naturally difficult to glue, e.g. polythene and nylon.

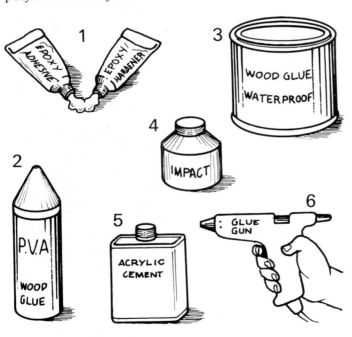

1 Epoxy adhesive is a commonly used metal glue. It comes in a two part pack containing the **adhesive** and a **hardener** which, once mixed, start setting because of a chemical reaction. It can be used on most rigid materials.

2 PVA wood adhesive (Poly-Vinyl Acetate). This is popular wood glue for indoor work. It can also be used on some other materials such as paper and card. It is a white glue that dries clear in about three hours. **It must not be used outdoors** as it is not waterproof.

3 Synthetic wood adhesive (waterproof). This is the wood glue to use if the joint is likely to get wet in use. It is usually supplied as a powder which is mixed with water to make a thick cream. Cascamite and Aerolite are two such glues.

4 Contact (impact) adhesive. This is a rubber-based glue which is flexible and can be used to stick flexible materials such as leather and cloth, as well as other materials such as Formica to plywood. It is called contact glue because it sticks on contact after being allowed to dry for a few minutes in the air.

5 Tensol cement – for acrylic. This glue is suitable for joining acrylic (perspex). It is a clear glue which air-dries quickly. Ensure a large gluing area for strong joints.

6 Glue gun. Glue sticks are manually fed into the gun where they are melted. The hot glue can be used to stick most materials including some of the difficult ones such as polythene. Once cold the joint is made.

Other adhesives of interest
PVC adhesive. A specialist PVC glue, this is mainly used for PVC piping in the construction industry.
Polystyrene adhesive. This produces very strong joints in solid polystyrene. It is often sold as aeromodelling cement. It *cannot* be used on expanded polystyrene because it dissolves it.
Balsa cement. This is a special fast setting balsawood glue, best used in thin layers.

NAILS AND NAILING

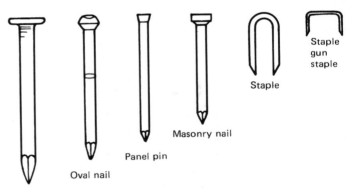

The **large round wire nail** is used for general joinery. **Oval wire nails** do not split the wood as easily as the round nails. **Panel pins** hold thin sheets (panels) of wood to thicker pieces of wood (e.g. for nailing box bases on). **Masonry nails** are specially hardened nails that can be used in bricks or concrete. **Staples** are used to hold wire netting or for jobs that need a loop.

Hints
To avoid the wood splitting, drill a hole in the top piece of wood a little smaller than the nail shank.
To hide small-headed nails, punch them about 2 mm below the surface with a **pin punch,** then fill the hole with wood filler.
To remove nails, use a pair of pincers or a claw hammer.

RIVETS

Rivets are mainly used to join two pieces of metal together. The most common are made from mild steel, but almost any soft metal can be used. If only one rivet is used it can act as a pivot. Traditionally riveting was very important for making ships etc., but nowadays electric spotwelding and arc welding are often used instead. Various rivet types are shown below; the dotted lines indicate the shape before riveting.

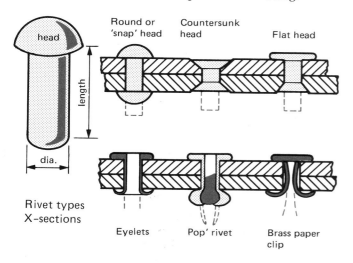

Rivet types
X-sections

PERMANENT WOOD JOINTS

Below are the joints used in **frame construction** (e.g. door and panel construction). Selection will depend on (a) strength required, (b) appearance and (c) how difficult it is to make. Below the **frame construction** are joints used in **box** or **carcase construction**.

Frame construction

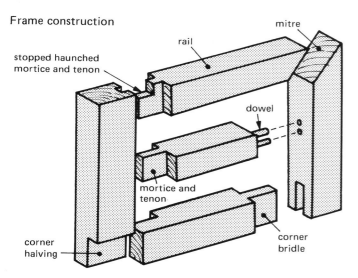

Box or carcase construction

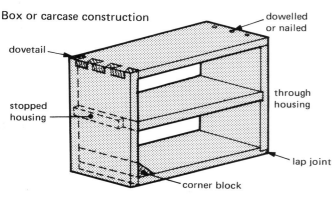

SOLDERING

Soldering is a hot method of joining metals using solder. The solder melts forming an **alloy** with the pieces being joined. **Flux** is used to keep the joint clean when hot; it also helps the solder flow into the joint.

1 SOFT SOLDERING

Soft soldering is used to join electric wires, printed circuits, copper, tinplate etc. The solder used is an alloy made from **lead** and **tin**; it melts at about 200°C.

Electricians' solder has flux in the centre; this avoids the need for separate flux. When soldering large pieces of metal **a large soldering iron will be needed.**

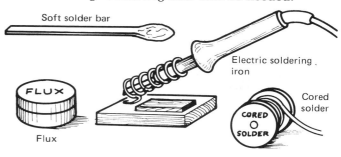

2 BRAZING

This form of soldering is much stronger than soft solder. The brazing rods used are an alloy of copper and zinc which melts at about 870°C.

To braze:

- Mix some brazing flux into a thick cream and apply it to the cleaned joint.
- Heat up as quickly as possible to bright red heat.
- Apply a fluxed brazing rod: the solder should flow into the joint.
- Cool slowly.

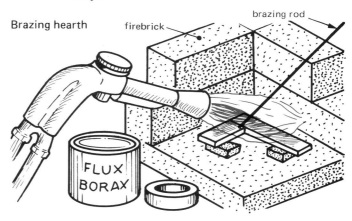

3 SILVER SOLDERING

Silver soldering is very similar to brazing except that it melts at a lower temperature and requires a different flux. This method is mainly used to join copper, brass and jewellery.

WELDING (materials joined by fusion)

Metals and some plastics can be welded. When welding either a filler rod is used or the two pieces to be joined can be welded together without a filler rod. **Oxy-acetylene welding** uses a gas to produce the heat needed to weld metals. **Electric arc welding** is faster than gas welding for welding steel. **Plastics welders** are used to weld plastics such as polythene.

Temporary joints

Temporary joints are used if the joint needs to be undone for any reason such as repairs, access, maintenance etc. There are hundreds of temporary joints on the market. A few are shown below.

Woodscrew types

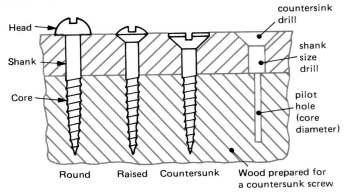

Head
Shank
Core
Round   Raised   Countersunk

countersink drill
shank size drill
pilot hole (core diameter)
Wood prepared for a countersunk screw

Nut and bolt types

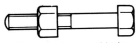

Hexagonal nut and bolt

Locknuts   Roundhead

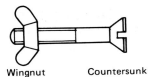

Wingnut   Countersunk

Split pinned castle nut   Cheese head

Other screw types

Sockethead grubsrew

Posidriv head setscrew

Self tapping screw. The hardened thread cuts its own thread

Washer types

Plain washer   Spring washer   Cup washer

Other temporary joints

'Snap on' top

Electric plug

Magnetic catch

Spring clip

Movable joints

Movable joints either move in a **straight line** or **rotate about an axis** (see examples below). Good bearings are needed if the parts are going to move a great deal (e.g. bike wheel bearings).

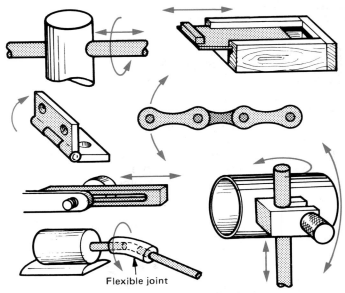

Flexible joint

A pupil-made compass that is holding a small knife being used to cut cardboard.

A BMX bicycle makes use of permanent, temporary and movable joints.

6 OBTAINING A GOOD SURFACE FINISH

The stages and methods used to obtain good surface finishes are described on this page. (See also page 116.)

Note A Only the common methods are shown below; other methods can also be used.

Note B When using glass paper or emery cloth, start with a grade that removes the last set of finishing marks quite easily, then go down through the finer grades.

Obtaining a good surface finish with wood

- Remove any saw marks with a 'smoothing plane' (the sides and edges only).
- Plane the end grain using a piece of scrap wood at the back to stop the wood splitting or use an 'abrasive wheel'.
- Use glass paper to finish off – always work 'with the grain' and remove any sharp edges (the glass paper being wrapped round a cork block).

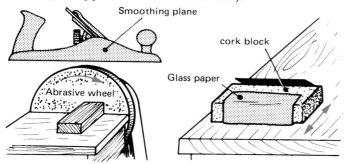

FINISHES THAT CAN BE APPLIED TO WOOD
Varnishes There are various varnishes available:
Polyurethane varnishes can withstand the effect of hot teapots, spillages etc.
French polish – a traditional varnish, now little used.
Yacht varnish is specially designed for outdoor use and boats.
Pre-catalysed lacquers are fast drying.

Paint Most paints can be used on wood, but remember to fill any holes and seal any knots with a sealer. If a very smooth finish is required each layer of paint will need to be smoothed down.

Stains Stains come in all colours and can be varnished as well.

Obtaining a good surface finish with metal

- Remove any saw marks starting with a coarse file and then a fine file.
- 'Drawfile' the metal to obtain a reasonably smooth finish.
- If an even finer finish is required it is usually obtained with emery cloth (the cloth being wrapped round a file).
- The easy-to-polish metals such as copper and brass can be given a mirror finish using a polishing machine.

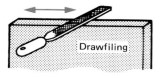

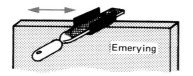

Polishing machine (guards not shown)

FINISHES THAT CAN BE APPLIED TO METALS
Some metals such as steel need an applied finish to prevent rust, corrosion and provide the final colour, but other metals such a gold and silver do not need this.

Paint For maximum protection, three coats should be applied: primer, undercoat and top coat. Gloss paint can be used but it is slow drying. Cellulose and enamel paints are fast drying.
Note Never use emulsion paint on steel because the water in the paint causes rust.

Oil A thin layer of oil provides temporary protection.

Bluing Steel is heated up until it is dark blue and then plunged into oil.

Lacquering This provides a thin, transparent varnish-like layer, sometimes applied to copper and brass etc.

Plastic dip coating Hot metal is dipped into a fluidised plastic powder for a few seconds. When removed, a plastic coating adheres to the metal (about 1.5 mm thick).

Obtaining a good surface finish with plastics

Note Hold the plastic carefully in soft jaws so as not to spoil the parts already polished.

- Remove any saw marks with a file or a smoothing plane.
- Depending on the type and thickness of the plastic it can be either (a) fine filed, (b) scraped with a scraper, or (c) a fine abrasive wheel can be used.
- Polish the plastic using either (a) fine 'wet and dry paper' (used wet), (b) a metal polish, or (c) a polishing machine.

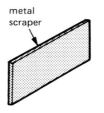

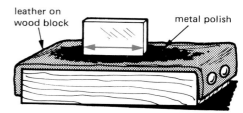

Polishing acrylic plastic with metal polish

Exercises

1 How would you obtain a good surface finish on: (a) a piece of wood, (b) a piece of sawn steel, (c) a piece of sawn acrylic? (See also page 116 for help.)
2 What adhesives would you use to join: (a) pinewood to pinewood for outdoor use, (b) leather to rubber, (c) acrylic to acrylic, (d) wood to cardboard, and (e) brass to steel?
3 Why do you think the following joining methods were used? (a) Copper wires soft soldered, (b) a nut used to hold on a bike wheel, (c) a rivet to join a piece of aluminium and brass together, (d) silver solder to join a brass and copper pendant.

This section deals with the following Technological subject areas:

MATERIALS BASED PROJECTS (pages 66–70)
STRUCTURES – theory and project ideas (pages 71–77)
MECHANISMS – theory and project ideas (pages 78–87)
ELECTRICS AND ELECTRONICS – theory and project ideas (pages 88–97)
COMPUTERS IN CDT (pages 98–102)
ENERGY – theory and project ideas (pages 103–107)
OTHER POPULAR PROJECTS (pages 108–111)

Other ideas for a wall plaque in model form. When making card models it is important to colour the parts similar to colours of the materials you hope to use.

MATERIALS BASED PROJECTS

The next few pages provide project ideas that encourage the use of a wide range of materials. Sample **design briefs** are given; if required they can be altered to suit your own requirements.
Note The **theory** of materials has already been covered in the last two sections (pages 45–61).

WALL PLAQUE PROJECT

A wall plaque made from the following design brief: 'Design and make a wall plaque that makes use of at least four different materials and has four different surface finishes.'

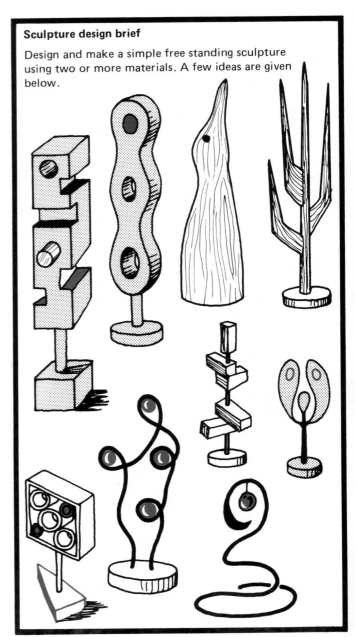

Sculpture design brief

Design and make a simple free standing sculpture using two or more materials. A few ideas are given below.

AN ELECTRIC CIRCUIT TESTER (12 V) AND SCREWDRIVER COMBINED

This is a more advanced project. The blade is made from special high carbon steel which is hardened and tempered. The handle is made from nylon rod which is drilled out so that an interior car bulb can fit inside. The screwed end cap is made from brass.

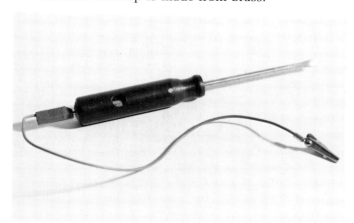

MONOGRAM DESIGN BRIEF

Design and make a monogram or similar using your initials, name, or a word of your own choice. It can be made as a separate project or used as part of another such as a badge or a nameplate. Some examples are shown below.

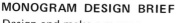

MODEL VEHICLE DESIGN BRIEF

Design and make a model vehicle of your own choice. Note – it must not be too complex to make, the wheels can either be bought or cut out with a hole saw. Below are a few ideas.

A hole saw like this can be used to make the wheels

Wheel and axle ideas

wheel

wheel

set screw

dowel axle

nail

CANDLE HOLDER

1 BRIEF

Design and make an attractive candle holder for one candle. To be used on the dining table or on the sideboard.

2 INVESTIGATION

(A) FUNCTIONS
To create a good atmosphere
To be safe in use, to be stable and fire resistant.
To be capable of being carried.

(B) QUESTIONS AND COMMENTS
How high should the flame be?
What type of candle will be used?

How will wax spillage be caught?
How will candle be held?

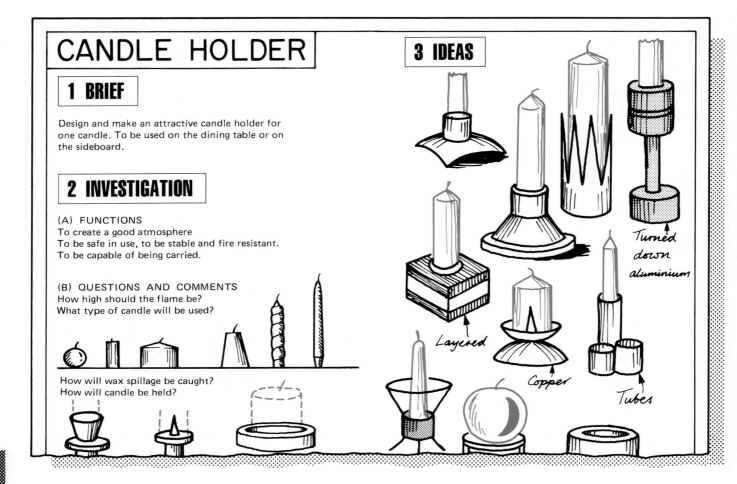

3 IDEAS

Turned down aluminium

Layered

Copper

Tubes

HOUSE NUMBER

1 BRIEF

Design and make:- (a) A HOUSE NUMBER for your house or (b) A number for some other use such as a classroom.

2 INVESTIGATION

Where will it be placed?
From what distance should it be seen?
What number styles could be used?
How will it be fixed in place?
What materials are suitable for use outdoors and in all weathers?
Will it be seen easily at night?
Can a light be used?

number styles

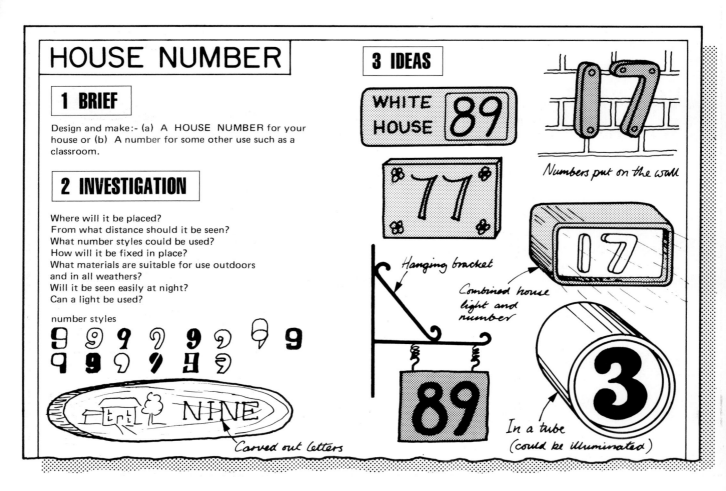

3 IDEAS

WHITE HOUSE 89

Numbers put on the wall

Hanging bracket

Combined house light and number

In a tube (could be illuminated)

Carved out letters

PENDANTS AND EARRINGS

DESIGN BRIEF
Design and make a pendant or an earring. It must make use of at least two different materials.

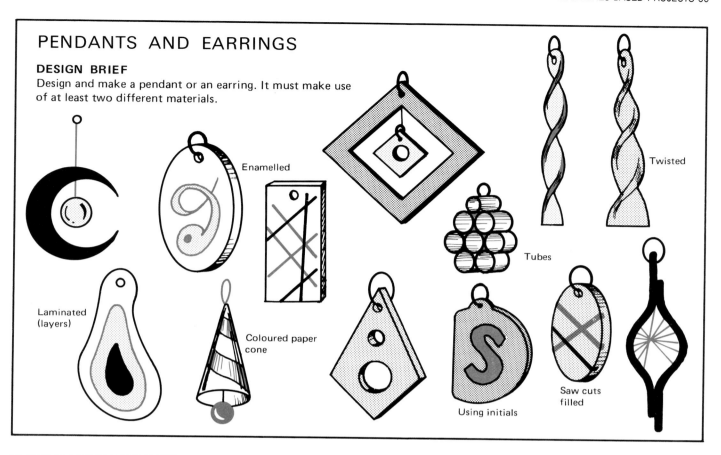

Enamelled

Twisted

Tubes

Laminated
(layers)

Coloured paper
cone

Using initials

Saw cuts
filled

IDEAS FOR SIMPLE CONTAINERS

DESIGN BRIEF
Design and make a simple container that can hold something of your choice, such as jewellery, money, a pack of cards, pens and pencils, a game, a clock mechanism, a favourite collection etc.

THINGS TO CONSIDER
Will a top and base be needed? What kind of lid is suitable (a lift-off, hinged or swivelled type)? Do the joints need to be hidden? How strong does it need to be? etc.

Below are containers made mainly from plastic and metal. On the next page are some container ideas mainly from wood.

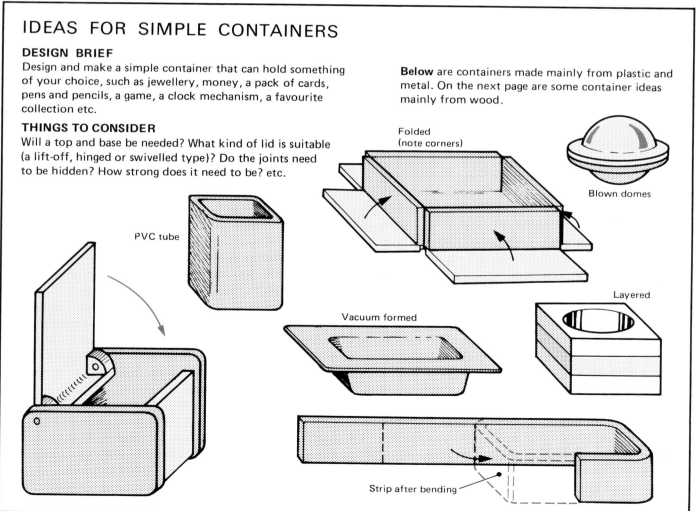

Folded
(note corners)

Blown domes

PVC tube

Vacuum formed

Layered

Strip after bending

IDEAS FOR SIMPLE CONTAINERS (CONTINUED)

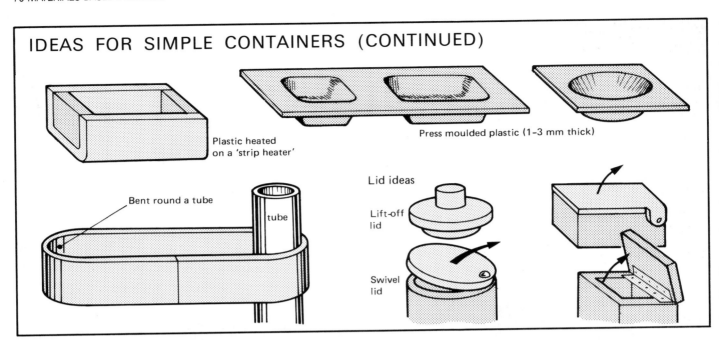

Plastic heated on a 'strip heater'

Press moulded plastic (1–3 mm thick)

Bent round a tube

tube

Lid ideas

Lift-off lid

Swivel lid

CONTAINER IDEAS: MAINLY WOOD

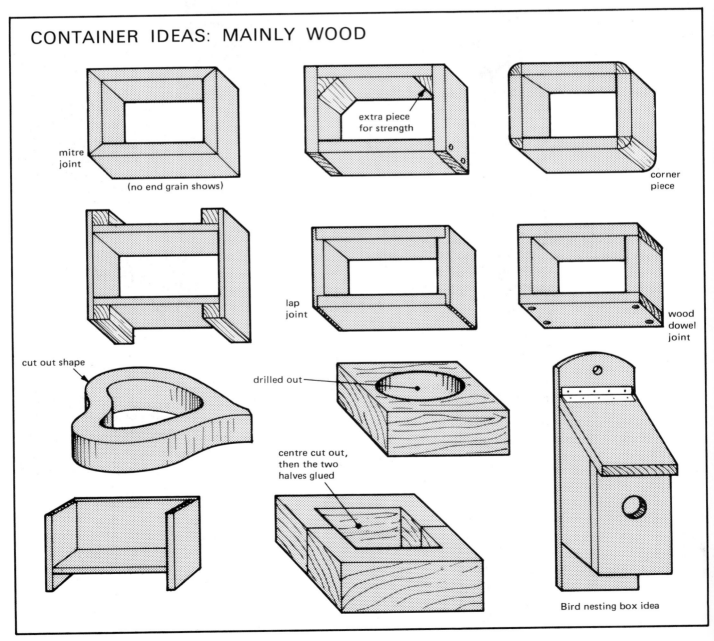

mitre joint

(no end grain shows)

extra piece for strength

corner piece

lap joint

wood dowel joint

cut out shape

drilled out

centre cut out, then the two halves glued

Bird nesting box idea

STRUCTURES

Structures are all around us – houses, bicycles, bridges, aircraft, chairs etc. This section of the book considers man-made structures. We can also learn a lot from natural structures such as plants and animals which have evolved over thousands of years.

Structures usually have one of the following uses:

- To support a load, e.g. a water tower.
- To span a gap, e.g. a bridge.
- To enclose objects or people, e.g. a car.

Note A A Practical Structures Course is included: the exercises are marked **S1** to **S18**.
Note B The unit of force used in structural calculations is the newton, symbol N.
The weight of 1 kg = 10 N approx.

A model skeleton made by a group of 11–12-year-old pupils at Hollinswood Middle School – an example of structures from nature.

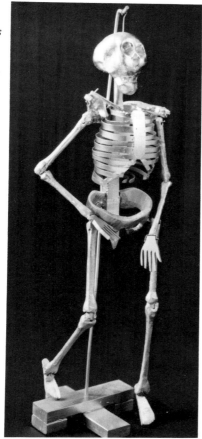

Gossamer Condor – the first man-powered aircraft to fly the English Channel.

Humber Bridge – the longest single span suspension bridge in the world.
What materials do you think it is made from?

Sailing dinghy. It must be able to withstand the effects of weather and being capsized.

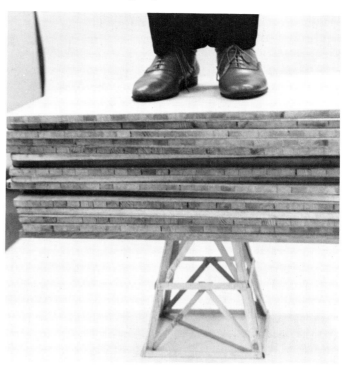

A wooden tower being tested. It actually carried six more pupils before it gave way!

Forces in structures: Basic theory

The forces in a structure result in the structure being in one or more of the following:

1 **Tension** and/or **compression**
2 **Bending**
3 **Shear**
4 **Torsion**

Forces are either **static** (not moving) or **dynamic** (moving). Static forces are not as destructive as the dynamic forces. Now try this:

S1   Stand on a beam (e.g. a piece of scrap wood) as shown below; the beam should be capable of supporting you. When you jump up and down, producing a dynamic force, the beam will probably break.

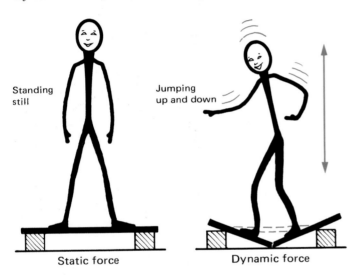

Standing still

Jumping up and down

Static force

Dynamic force

1 TENSION AND COMPRESSION
Materials that are pulled are said to be in **tension**; materials that are pushed are said to be in **compression**.

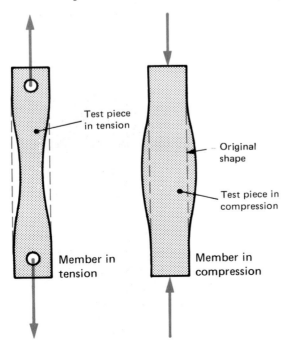

Test piece in tension

Original shape

Test piece in compression

Member in tension

Member in compression

In structural work the parts that are in tension are called **ties** (ties are usually thinner than parts that have to resist compressive forces). The parts that have to resist compressive forces are called **struts.**

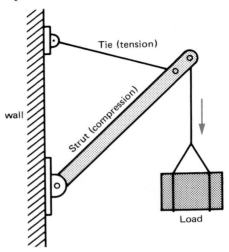

Tie (tension)

wall

Strut (compression)

Load

A jib crane showing its tie and strut

Buckling
The illustration below shows a tube that has buckled.

S2   Using only one sheet of A4 paper, make a form that can support as large a load as possible without buckling.

S3   Repeat S2, but this time you can use a 100 mm piece of tape as well.

2 BENDING
Examples of planks bending are shown below. The larger the force the more the plank will bend unless the material is rigid enough to resist the force. (See page 74 for more details on making beams more rigid.)

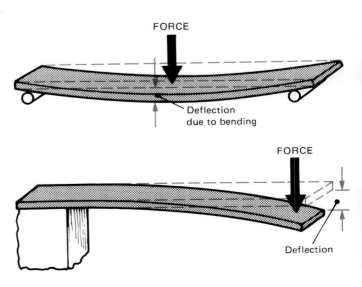

FORCE

Deflection due to bending

FORCE

Deflection

3 SHEAR

When a pair of scissors is used to cut some card, it is actually shearing the card. Shearing forces try to move one part of the material past another part.

A towbar pin shown in 'shear'

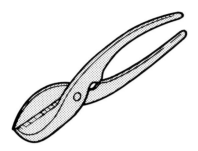

Metal shears used to cut sheet metal

4 TORSION

This is a twisting force: if you pick up your ruler and twist it as shown, it is said to be in **torsion.**

A ruler in torsion

Triangulation

A **triangular** shape is a strong **rigid** shape and is therefore used a great deal in structural work.

S4 Using strips of card, or similar, make the triangular shape below using only one pin in each corner.

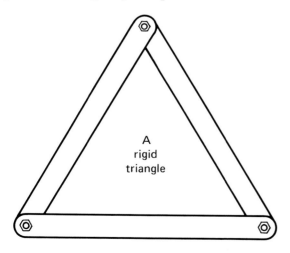

A
rigid
triangle

Other shapes made from strips are not rigid unless they have some form of **triangulation** in them. To make unstable shapes rigid, an extra tie or strut can be added in the correct place to make it rigid by triangulation.

A pin-jointed rectangle is unstable and easy to move about:

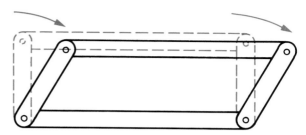

S5 Make a pin-jointed rectangle, or square, like the one shown above, and then make it rigid using (a) one extra strip of material, or (b) more than one strip. Some possible ideas are shown below:

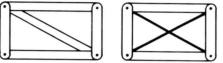
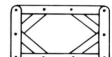

S6 Assemble this house-like shape using 'pin joints' and then make it rigid with the least number of strips.

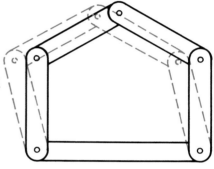

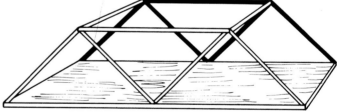

A simple bridge (note triangulation)

S7 Try to make a bike frame using card strips and card discs for the wheels.

Racing cycle, Olympic style. What differences can you spot from a normal road bike?

Beams

Beams are used a great deal in structural work to span gaps and support a load. A beam's stiffness is dependent on the material used and its position.

S8 Place a ruler as shown below in (A) and it will bend easily, but if it is placed on its edge as shown in (B) it is very resistant to bending.

Bending of beams

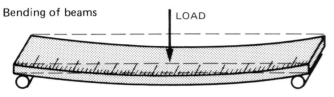

(A) The ruler bends easily

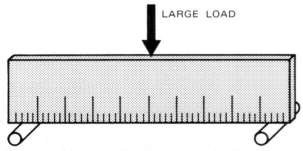

(B) A ruler on its edge is much stiffer and resists bending

The bottom surface of a beam must be able to resist tensile forces (pulling forces) and the top of a beam must resist compressive forces (pushing forces). This is demonstrated by the bending of sponge as shown in (C). The dotted line in the centre is called the **neutral axis** where there are no tensile or compressive forces.

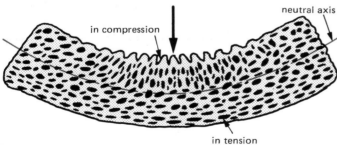

(C) Sponge being bent

Strong beam sections commonly used

I-section beam — a very strong and economical use of materials

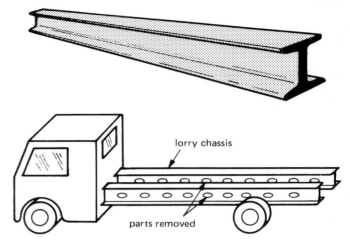

Note Material can be removed from the neutral axis area, making very little difference to the strength of the beam.

S9 Using one sheet of card, span a distance 10 mm shorter than the longest length of the card. Experiment with scrap pieces of paper first. Some ideas are given below.

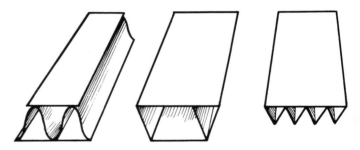

CONCRETE BEAMS

Concrete is very strong in compression but weak in tension. This means a concrete beam is weak unless it is reinforced with steel near the bottom edge where the tension forces are greatest and would normally break the concrete.

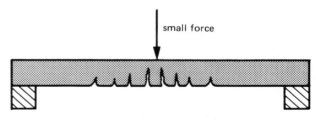

(A) Concrete beams without extra reinforcement break very easily

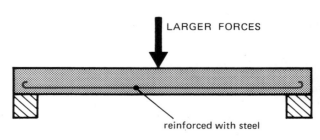

(B) Reinforced concrete is much stronger

Bridges

S10 Design and make a bridge to span 600 mm using the materials provided by your teacher. Then test to see how much it can carry. (See Testing, page 28.)

Stone slab beam bridge

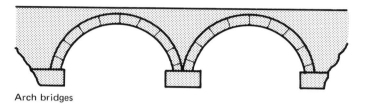
Arch bridges

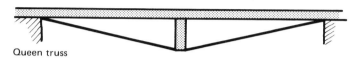
Queen truss

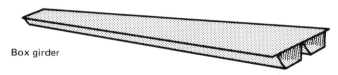
Box girder

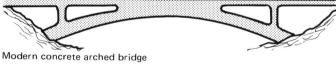
Modern concrete arched bridge

Model of an arched bridge

S11 Design a suspension type bridge to span 2 metres and to carry as large a load as possible in the centre. Ends will need to be attached.

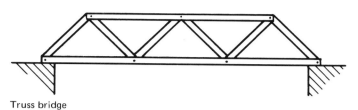
Truss bridge

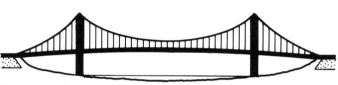
Cantilever bridge (each side of the bridge balances the other side)

Suspension bridge

Pupils modelling a suspension bridge using a car tow rope

A model of the world's first iron bridge which spans the River Severn, originally constructed by Abraham Derby III. The model was built by a class of 11-year-old pupils at Hollinswood Middle School and made from thick card with painted acrylic for the railings.

A model of a footbridge next to Telford town centre which spans a road. The model was built by a class of 11-year-old pupils at Hollinswood Middle School. Materials used were wood, card, string and concrete.

Bridges (continued)

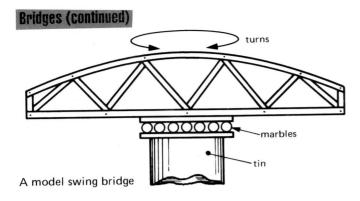

turns

marbles

tin

A model swing bridge

Modelling materials

When making models, try to use modelling materials that have similar properties to that of the materials of the real bridge being modelled, e.g. concrete could be represented by plaster of paris or clay. Parts in tension must not be too stretchy, thin wire could be used.
Note A glue-gun can save a lot of construction time

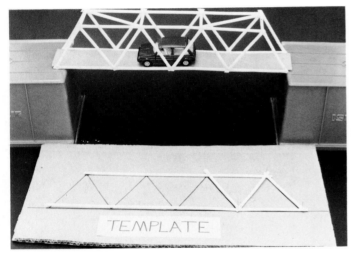

TEMPLATE

Model of a bridge being made from Artstraws – note how the sides are first constructed on a template.

Testing: Bridges, towers, beams etc.

Models can either be tested to destruction or tested for a specific property such as the amount of deflection (the amount moved due to the load). It can be great fun making a model and then testing it to destruction. The following formula is often used to decide the best model.

$$\text{Best-model ratio} = \frac{\text{maximum load carried}}{\text{weight of structure}}$$

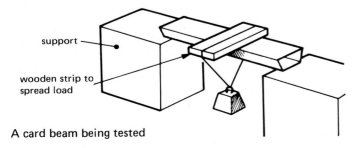

support

wooden strip to spread load

A card beam being tested

Towers

A successful tower will resist **buckling** and will not fall over easily.

S12 In groups, make 10 shapes that resist buckling similar to those shown below, then tape them all together to see how much they can support. You may be able to sit on them! A4 writing paper can be used.

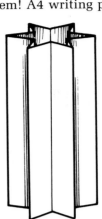
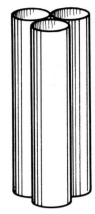

S13 Make a structure that can support a ball as high as possible, given one sheet of card, tape and string.

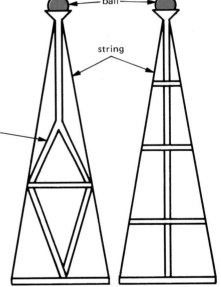

ball

string

some of the card made into tubes

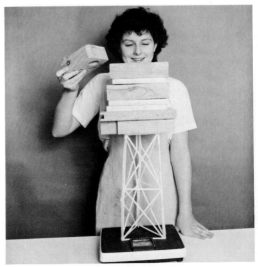

Tower made from Artstraws being tested.

Other ideas for projects

S14   First make the **tetrahedron** form below, using straws and pipe-cleaners for the joints. Then make a more adventurous model of your own.

Geometric models

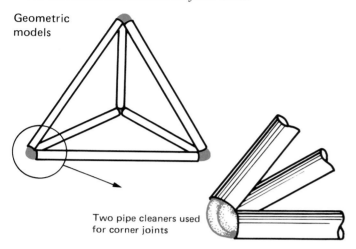

Two pipe cleaners used for corner joints

A CRANE

S15   Design and make a free-standing (not fixed) crane – the lighter it is the better – that can support a 0.5 kg weight at least 400 mm from the ground and reaching out 200 mm from the footings as shown in the outline below.

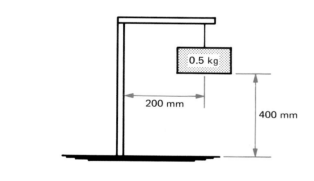

0.5 kg

200 mm

400 mm

IDEAS

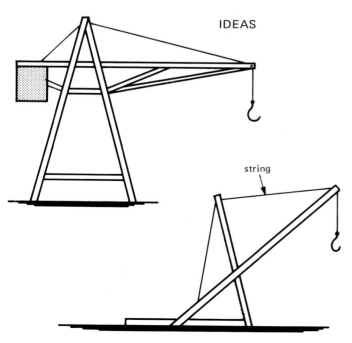

string

KITES

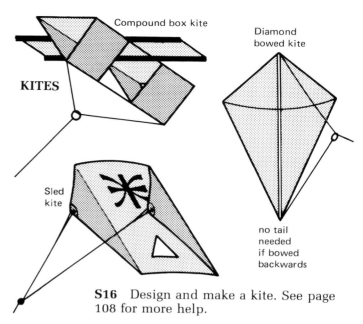

Compound box kite

Diamond bowed kite

Sled kite

no tail needed if bowed backwards

S16   Design and make a kite. See page 108 for more help.

S17   Make a marble jump (like a ski jump) out of one sheet of card. The aim is to make a marble jump as far as possible. One idea is shown below.

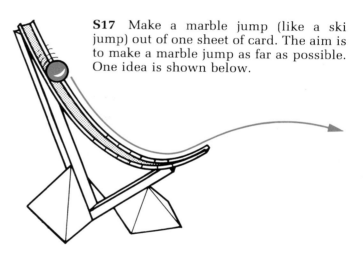

S18   Make a model of a quick-to-assemble house suitable for use in a disaster area. The cover need only be plastic sheeting.

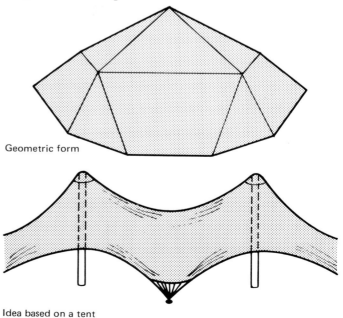

Geometric form

Idea based on a tent

MECHANISMS

This section includes:

1 **Basic theory of mechanisms** (pages 79–83)
2 **A practical mechanisms course** (page 84)
3 **Project examples** (pages 86–87)

A **mechanism** is a way of changing one kind of force into another kind of force from one place to another and includes levers, gears, pulleys, cams, cranks etc.

Machines are made up of one or more mechanisms to solve a particular problem; they can only work when energy is applied.

Mechanisms are used because:
1 They are very versatile.
2 They are efficient (if good bearings are used).
3 Sometimes there is no alternative but to use a mechanism.

Reasons for not using mechanisms are:
1 They need maintenance, e.g. oiling.
2 The moving parts may be dangerous.
3 Rubbing parts are liable to wear.
4 Other methods may be better (e.g. mechanical calculators have been replaced by electronic calculators).

A BASIC PRACTICAL MECHANISMS COURSE —

is provided on page 84. It can be completed using a construction kit such as the Fischertechnik or LEGO® technical kits.

Note *It is advisable to read the next few pages before starting the course.*

This page introduces mechanisms by showing various mechanisms you could make.

Pantograph made from acrylic plastic that allows drawings to be increased or decreased in size.

A cheap, easy to make mechanism based on a system developed by the author. The eyes and the nose on the face rotate when the handle is turned. The mechanism is made from card, welding rod, large dowel and elastic bands.

A walking robot made using a LEGO technical kit.

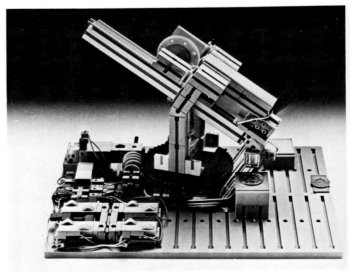

A robotic arm controlled by a computer. It is based on Fischertechnik components.

1 BASIC THEORY OF MECHANISMS

Levers

Levers consist of a **beam** that can rotate about a fixed point called a **pivot** or **fulcrum**. Levers are used in three basic ways as shown below. In use, the **load** is moved by an **effort** being applied. If the beam stays still, the forces are equal and are said to be in **equilibrium**. In other words, the forces tending to turn the beam one way are equal to the forces tending to turn it the other way.

The **three basic classes** (or **types**) of lever are shown below, the difference being the way the **pivot, load** and **effort** are arranged.

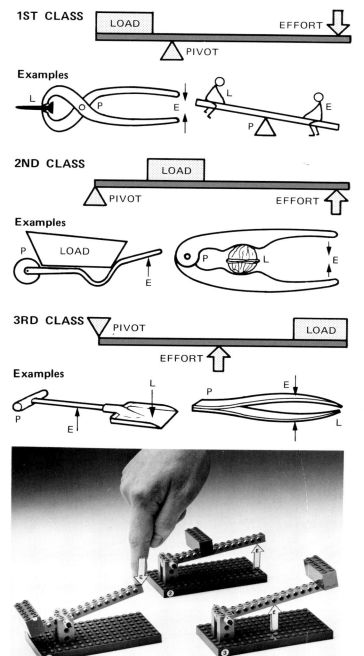

Examples showing the three types of lever – LEGO® technical kit used.

Moments

This is the word used to describe the turning effect caused by a force on a lever. The effect of the turning force on a lever is dependent on the **distance of the force from the pivot**. This can be written down as follows:

> **moment = force × distance from pivot**

When a beam is not moving (when it is in **equilibrium**), the **anti-clockwise moments** are equal to the **clockwise moments**.

The beam below is in equilibrium because:

anti-clockwise moments = clockwise moments
$$5\ N \times 4\ m = 2\ N \times 10\ m$$
20 Nm = 20 Nm

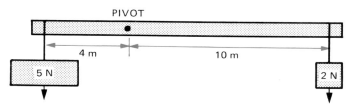

Mechanical advantage

This is the ratio between the **effort** needed and the **load**. The formula is written down as:

> **mechanical advantage** $= \dfrac{\textbf{load}}{\textbf{effort}}$

Question: What would the mechanical advantage (MA) be if 100 newtons is needed to lift a load of 400 newtons?

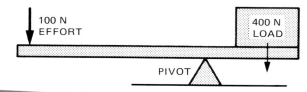

Velocity ratio

Levers can make the lifting of a large load easy, but the **distance** moved by the **effort** will be more than that moved by the **load**.

The **velocity ratio** is the **distance moved by the load** compared to the **distance moved by the effort**.

> **velocity ratio** $= \dfrac{\textbf{distance moved by effort}}{\textbf{distance moved by load}}$

Question: What is the velocity ratio (VR) of the beam below?

Changing the direction of motion

Mechanisms can be used to change the direction of motion. Some methods commonly used are shown below.

The larger red arrows indicate the normal input motion.

Question: How many mechanisms below have a rotary input and a reciprocating 'back-and-forth' output?

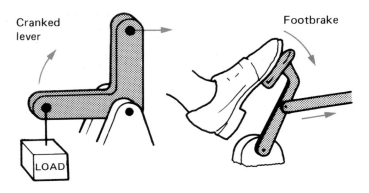

Cranked lever

LOAD

Footbrake

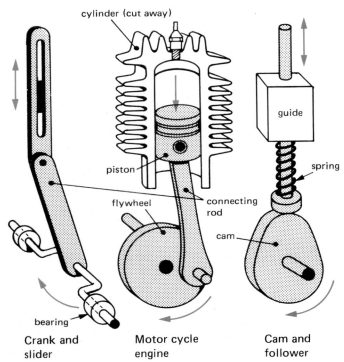

cylinder (cut away)

guide

piston

spring

flywheel

connecting rod

cam

bearing

Crank and slider

Motor cycle engine

Cam and follower

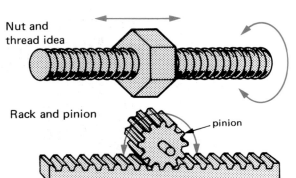

Nut and thread idea

Rack and pinion

pinion

Pulleys

Pulleys are often used to change the direction of forces.

A single (fixed) pulley
A pulley used to change the direction of a force.

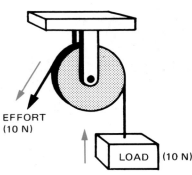

EFFORT (10 N)

LOAD (10 N)

A winding drum
(as used in old wells)

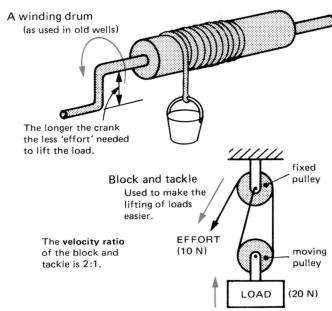

The longer the crank the less 'effort' needed to lift the load.

Block and tackle
Used to make the lifting of loads easier.

The **velocity ratio** of the block and tackle is 2:1.

EFFORT (10 N)

fixed pulley

moving pulley

LOAD (20 N)

Belt drives

Belt drives are very versatile but have the disadvantage of slipping (this can also be used as an advantage, e.g. a safety factor if something jams up).

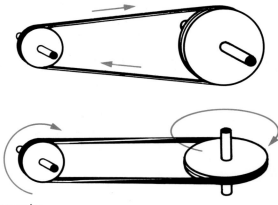

A 90 degree twist

Examples using levers, pulleys etc.

A mechanism used to make a moving picture (insert shows rear view).

Perhaps you could make something similar.

A model mechanical saw. What happens when the motor turns?

Below is a model of a harmonograph. It is a mechanism used to make random patterns on paper.

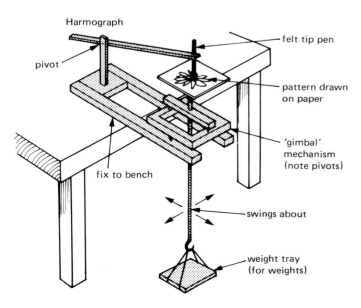

A fun nut cracker made from a LEGO® technical kit. Can you see the crank, the pulley and the cranked lever?

Chain drives

The chain runs on sprockets to provide a very positive drive with no slip. It is a very efficient system which is why it is used on bicycles.

Close-up of a bicycle chain drive. Can you see the tensioning device?

A simplified model of a two-speed bicycle chain drive made using a LEGO® technical kit.

Gears and gearing

Gears are an important means of transmitting movement. Gears can be very efficient if the teeth are meshed together properly and the shafts have good bearings. Mechanism kits used in schools do not have very good bearings when compared with the gears used in mechanical watches and clocks, which are very efficient. When using gears it is important to realise that the direction of rotation changes from one gear to the next as shown below.

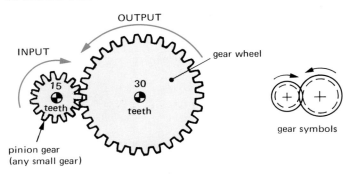

Two gears meshed together change the direction of rotation.

A LEGO® technical kit used to assemble two meshing gears.

GEAR RATIOS

Gearing up means that the output gear turns faster than the input gear, but less force is available.

Gearing down means that the output gear turns slower than the input gear (but more force is available).

To find out what the **gear ratio** (GR) is for two gears, the following formula is used:

$$\text{gear ratio} = \frac{\text{number of teeth on input gear}}{\text{number of teeth on output gear}}$$

Example question: What is the gear ratio of the two gears above?

$$\text{gear ratio} = \frac{15 \text{ teeth}}{30 \text{ teeth}}$$

$$\text{Answer} = \frac{1}{2} \text{ or } \textbf{a 1:2 ratio}$$

Question: What would the gear ratio be if the input gear has 200 teeth and the output gear had 50 teeth?

GEAR TRAINS

Two or more gears joined together form a **gear train**. Below is an example of a gear train. If the centre gear is used only to change the direction of rotation or to act as a 'spacer' it is called an **idler** gear.

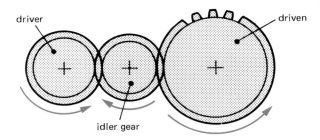

A LEGO technical kit used to make a gear train.

BEVEL GEARS

These are used to transmit motion through an angle, usually 90°, as shown below.

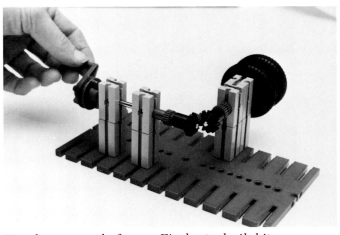

Bevel gears made from a Fischertechnik kit.

WORM AND WHEEL GEARS

Worm and wheel gears transmit motion through 90° as shown below. One very useful property of worm and wheel gears is that a **very low gear reduction** is achieved. This makes them ideal for reducing the speed of electric motors using only two gears. If the large gear has 40 teeth the gear ratio will be 1 to 40. Can you see why only the worm wheel can be used to input the motion?

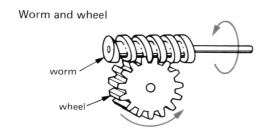

Worm and wheel

worm

wheel

Model vehicle made from a LEGO® technical kit. Worm and wheel gearing is used to obtain a large gear reduction.

Other mechanisms

Ratchet and pawl

The pawl allows the shaft to turn only one way (e.g. a bike freewheel)

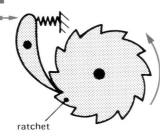

ratchet

Universal joint

Universal joints are used to transmit rotary action when shafts are not exactly 'in line'.

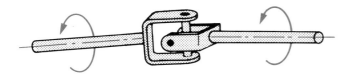

Flexible coupling

As above, but for light loads only.

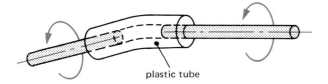

plastic tube

How fast will it go?

Sometimes you need to know how fast a vehicle will travel (in theory) along the floor. Below is an example calculation.

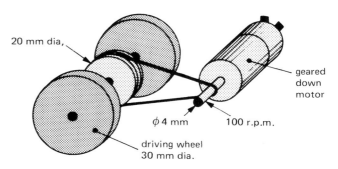

20 mm dia.

geared down motor

φ 4 mm   100 r.p.m.

driving wheel 30 mm dia.

SPEED OF VEHICLE CALCULATION

1st stage

Find out how fast the driving wheels turn by using the following formula (see page 79 for explanation):

$$\textbf{velocity ratio} = \frac{\textbf{diameter of driving pulley}}{\textbf{diameter of driven pulley}}$$

$$\text{velocity ratio} = \frac{4 \text{ mm (motor drive)}}{20 \text{ mm (pulley on axle)}}$$

$$\text{velocity ratio} = \frac{1}{5}$$

$$\text{rear axle turns} = \frac{1}{5} \times 100 \text{ RPM (RPM = revolutions per minute)}$$

$$= 20 \text{ RPM}$$

2nd stage

For each revolution the vehicle travels the circumference of the wheel:

$$\boxed{\textbf{circumference} = \textbf{3.14} \times \textbf{diameter}}$$

circumference = 3.14 × 30 mm = 94.2 mm

Answer: distance per minute = 20 RPM × 94.2 mm = 1184 mm/min = **1.8 metres per minute.**

Electrically driven vehicle (underneath view). Note that the drive is similar to that used in the example shown above.

2 A PRACTICAL MECHANISMS COURSE

The following course can be completed using a construction kit such as the Fischertechnik or LEGO® technical construction kits. Only the outline of a problem or activity is shown; if more help is needed, refer to the previous pages where some of the answers can be found as photographs, etc.

For each mechanism made, make a sketch, like the ones illustrated on this page, together with **notes of your observations.**

1 Start by becoming familiar with the kit you are going to use. See how many different parts you can make use of (by joining together) in the time allowed.

2 Assemble the lever mechanism below with a **load** on the short end. Then add weights to the longer end until it balances. Which end has the heavier weight? (See page 79 for help.)

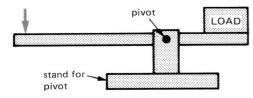

3 Make a wheelbarrow similar to that below. Then move the wheels to the front. Is more effort now required to lift the load?

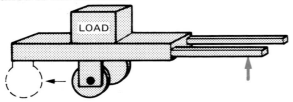

4 Make the mechanism below as shown (note the long ends and the short ends). Then see what difference there is when end (b) is moved instead of end (a).

5 Assemble the example of **rotary to linear** motion shown below. Add a heavy wheel to act as a **flywheel** and see what difference it makes. (See pages 80 and 81 for help.)

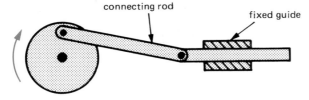

6 Assemble the **rack and pinion** mechanism shown below (guides will be needed for the rack to move in).

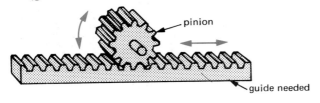

7 Make a tall supporting frame, then add the two pulleys as shown to make a **block and tackle** mechanism. What is the **velocity ratio** of the pulley system?

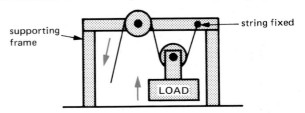

8 Assemble the pulley system below. How much faster does the small pulley turn than the larger pulley?

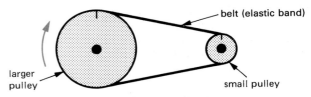

9 Using the same pulley wheels, put the pulley belt on with a 180° twist in it as shown below. What difference does this make?

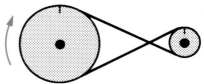

10 Assemble a large gear and a small gear. Do they turn easier than the pulley wheels just made in **8** and **9**?

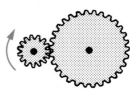

11 Assemble a **compound gear train** as shown below. Note that the two middle gears are on the same centre shaft. What effect does the extra gearing have on the speed of the larger gear?

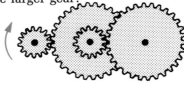

EXTRA

Make a mechanism that achieves the following movements:

12   **13**

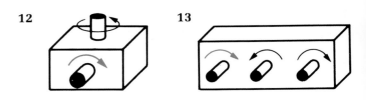

14 Make a vehicle that can be steered.

15 Make a vehicle that is powered by an electric motor.

16 Make a slow-moving vehicle powered by an electric motor, and then see how steep a slope it can climb.

17 Make a vehicle that makes use of a **differential gear system** (if your kit has one).

Hints on making your own mechanisms

Sometimes a permanent cheap method of construction is needed. Below are some well-tried methods. Quite a few constructional methods can produce poor results because the shafts used are too large in diameter. Try to use small diameter steel rod rather than large diameter wooden dowel for shafts.

A useful size is 4 mm because Meccano and Fischertechnik parts can be used if required.

Note The sizes given assume 4 mm rod is being used.

MAKING A MECHANISM CONTAINER

1 Place the mechanism, e.g. pulley wheels, in place as shown below, and mark off the hole positions accurately on one of the side pieces.

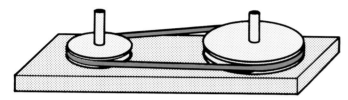

Deciding where to put the pulleys

2 Drill the holes needed carefully, making sure the two side pieces are held together firmly. (Tape, elastic bands or a clamp could be used.)

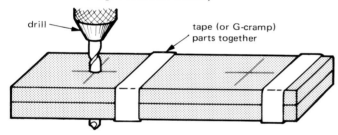

3 Assemble the mechanism with any extra pieces needed, e.g. a base. Make sure one side can be easily and quickly removed, to allow easy access to the mechanism for alterations etc.

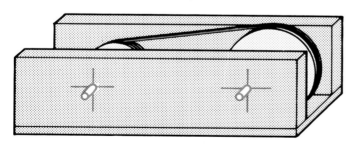

WHEELS AND PULLEYS

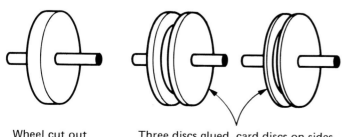

Wheel cut out with a hole saw

Three discs glued, card discs on sides

MAKING WHEELS, PULLEYS AND DISCS ETC.

Wheels, pulleys and discs can be made from almost any material, for example cardboard, wood and acrylic. To make the discs a **holesaw** can be used. Thin card can be cut with a **knife held in a compass. Old tin lids** can also be used; the centre can be found accurately with a **centre finder.**

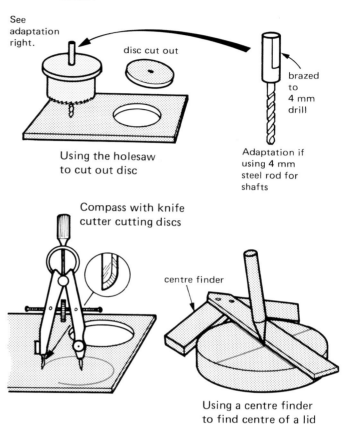

See adaptation right.

disc cut out

brazed to 4 mm drill

Using the holesaw to cut out disc

Adaptation if using 4 mm steel rod for shafts

Compass with knife cutter cutting discs

centre finder

Using a centre finder to find centre of a lid

MOUNTING ELECTRIC MOTORS

The main mounting methods used are: nuts and bolts, gluing, PVC tape, elastic bands. The last two methods are shown below.

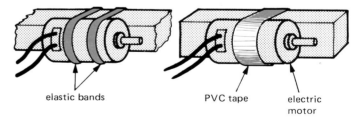

elastic bands

PVC tape

electric motor

COLLARS AND SPACERS

Made from scrap plastic etc.

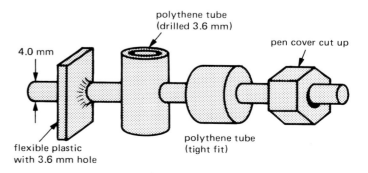

polythene tube (drilled 3.6 mm)

pen cover cut up

4.0 mm

flexible plastic with 3.6 mm hole

polythene tube (tight fit)

3 PROJECT EXAMPLES

The following project examples use the construction methods described on page 85. See also page 106 for a few more similar ideas.

Electric motor-driven vehicle

Note No permanent joints are used.

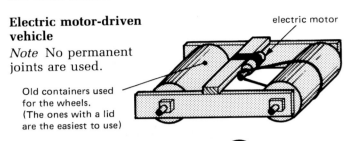

electric motor

Old containers used for the wheels. (The ones with a lid are the easiest to use)

A mobile crane built on a basic frame

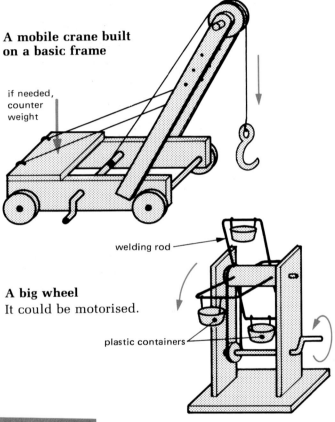

if needed, counter weight

welding rod

A big wheel

It could be motorised.

plastic containers

Design brief

Design and make a toy that makes something 'pop up and down' as it is pulled along. The following ideas may help you.

A fork-lift truck

Could a ratchet be used to hold the forks in place?

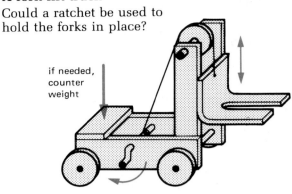

if needed, counter weight

A light flasher

The contacts can be made from metal strip.

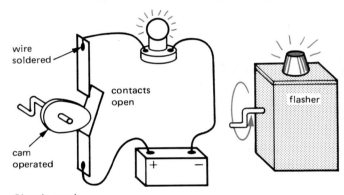

wire soldered

contacts open

cam operated

flasher

Circuit used

A windmill

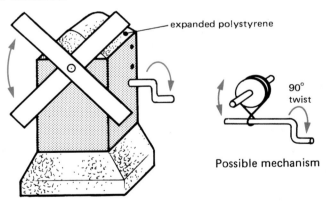

expanded polystyrene

90° twist

Possible mechanism

A three-speed vehicle made from old containers, wood and 4 mm steel rod. The pulleys are made from dowel and card discs glued together.

Design brief A

Design and make a simple **weighing machine** that makes use of leverage to weigh things of your own choice (without using extra weights).

Investigation questions and help

What will it weigh? (parcels, food etc.)
What size should it be?
What is the minimum and maximum load likely to be?
How accurate does the scale have to be? (Will the divisions be read in grams or kilograms?)
What could cause a false reading to be given? (e.g. friction in the bearings and parts that catch.)

To alter the sensitivity the pivot is moved.

Calibration

To put an accurate scale on your weighing machine it will need to be calibrated against a set of known weights or scales. *Note* The diagrams opposite illustrate the basic theory involved. Also see the photograph on page 28.

IDEAS

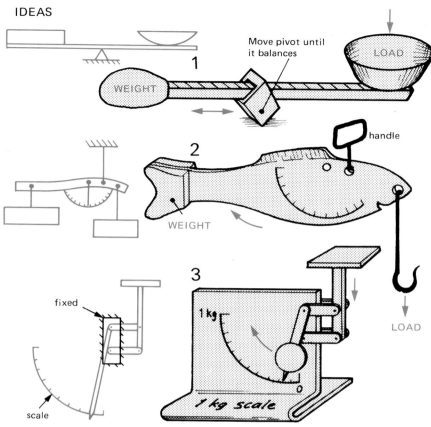

Design brief B

Design and make a pair of **proportional dividers** for transferring drawings. (If a pencil is attached instead of one of the points, it can be used as a compass as well.)

IDEAS

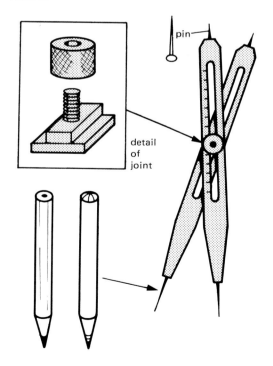

A pen or pencil, for converting into a compass

Design brief C

Design and make a pull toy using the examples below to help you. *Note* The moving parts must return to their original positions when the pull string is pulled, then released. Also see the photograph on page 26.

IDEAS

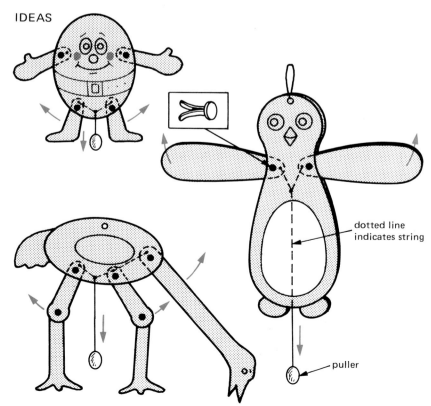

dotted line indicates string

puller

ELECTRICS AND ELECTRONICS

How would you like to live in a world without electricity, good lighting, washing machines, televisions, radios and computers etc., as we know them today?

Electricity is used to
— provide heat and light.
— provide a magnetic effect (electro-magnetism); electric motors and bells make use of this effect.
— produce a chemical change such as electroplating of chromium.
— carry information along wires, e.g. telephones and radios.

Electrical safety

High voltage electricity (mains electricity) must be treated with great respect as it can kill by **electrocution**. For this reason, only low voltage electricity should be used, unless you are a qualified electrician and know what you are doing.

This section is arranged as follows:

Electrics (pages 89–92)
Electronics (pages 93–95)
Project ideas (pages 96–97)

There is a **symbols summary chart** on p. 97.

A simple radio made by a 14-year-old pupil.

An easy-to-make vehicle used to mount the motorised circuits given on page 92.

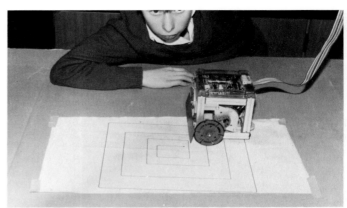

A computer-controlled robot that can perform various tasks, for example draw on the floor as shown here, or following a light beam etc.

Practical course work

The circuits described on the next few pages can be used as a basic electrics and electronics course. It is advisable to work through the electrics course before starting the electronics course, but this is not absolutely necessary. If time is limited and money is restricted the circuits can be demonstrated by the teacher or used as part of a rotation within the class.

Parts list

ELECTRIC PARTS
— needed for pages 89–92.

3 **batteries** 4.5 V
1 **battery** 9 V
3 **bulbs and bulb holders** 6 V 0.06 A or similar
  resistors ¼ watt type. A range of resistors, e.g. 10 Ω, 100 Ω, 1 kΩ (3), 10 kΩ (3), 100 kΩ
3 **variable resistors** 10 kΩ, 100 kΩ and 22 kΩ
2 **light dependent resistors** (ORP 12)
1 **thermistor** (a heat sensitive resistor)
2 **small d.c. motors** low voltage (one low geared)
3 **switches** (single-pole-single-throw type)
1 **switch** (double-pole-double-throw type)
1 **rotary switch** with at least four contacts (positions)
1 **reed switch** and **magnet**
2 **microswitches** (one to be lever operated)
1 **bell** or **buzzer** 6 V or 12 V (low power type)
1 **solenoid** 12 V max.
1 **relay** 5 V or 12 V DPDT type
1 **capacitor** 5000 µF

Other – voltmeter, ammeter (0–1 A) and a vehicle on which to mount circuits **(19)**, **(20)** and **(21)**.

EXTRA PARTS
—needed for electronic circuits on pages 94 and 95.

1 **speaker** 75 Ω (or 8 Ω with 68 Ω resistor in series)
1 **diode** general purpose type, e.g. IN 4001
  transistors general purpose types
6 **transistors** BC 108
1 **transistor** BFY 51
2 **capacitors** 0.1 µF
2 **capacitors** 220 µF
1 **counter** (optional)

ELECTRICS

Electrics in this book means circuits without semi-conductors such as transistors, but including electro-magnetic devices such as motors and relays.

A practical electrics course

The circuits numbered can form the basis of a practical electrics course.

Basic electrics theory

Voltage, V, can be thought of as the pressure pushing electricity along the wire and is measured with a voltmeter. The greater the force, the greater the voltage. If a 4.5 V battery is connected up to a 6 V bulb it will glow dimly, but if the voltage is increased by connecting up a second battery in **series** as shown, the bulb will glow brightly. The total voltage going to the bulb is now 9 V.

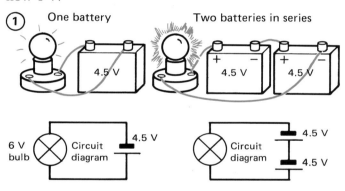

BATTERIES CONNECTED IN PARALLEL

If, instead of connecting up the batteries in series as shown above, they are connected up in **parallel**, the voltage is still 4.5 V (but more current is available to the circuit if required).

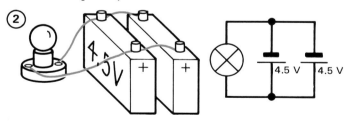

MEASURING VOLTAGE

To measure the voltage the probes of the voltmeter are placed either side of a **load**, such as a bulb or motor. (The low reading on the meter below means the battery is old.)

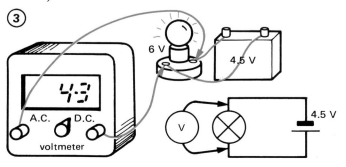

ELECTRIC CURRENT

Electric current (symbol I) can be considered as the speed of electricity flowing through a circuit. It is measured in **amperes**, A ('amps' for short), with an **ammeter**. The current flowing in a circuit depends on the resistance to the flow by the components in the circuit.

If a large current is to flow through a wire, a thick wire will be required to prevent the wire heating up and melting the plastic casing, e.g. a car starter motor wire is very thick because it has to carry up to 150 amps; in contrast the wires going to the same car's sidelights are thin, because they only need to carry about 3 amps.

MEASURING CURRENT

To measure electric current an **ammeter** is placed 'in circuit' as shown below. *Be careful!* Ammeters are easily damaged, so start with a **high** setting on the ammeter.

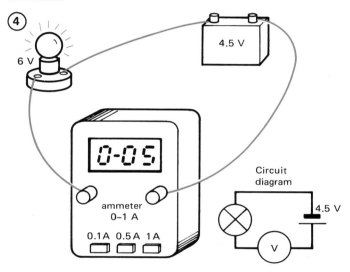

What current does the bulb actually use?

ELECTRIC POWER

Power is measured in **watts**, W. It is the rate of doing work. Electric power is found by multiplying the voltage with the current being used at any one instant.

power (watts) = voltage (volts) × current (amps)

Example: Find the power required to turn a 12 volt car starter motor if it consumes 80 amps.
Answer: Power = 12 volts × 80 amps = 960 watts.

Question: Find the power required by a 12 volt car headlight bulb if it consumes 4 amps.

Question: How much power does the bulb just used in diagram 4 above consume?

A.C. AND D.C. ELECTRICITY

The letters a.c. stands for **alternating current**, the type of electricity that we obtain from the Electricity Board (mains electricity). The letters d.c. stand for **direct current**, the type of electricity we obtain from batteries. When using a meter to measure d.c. current, make sure it is set on the d.c. setting.

Resistors (and resistive components)

Resistors restrict the flow of electricity, rather like a tap that restricts the water supply. The resistance value is measured in **ohms**, Ω. Resistors can be bought as **fixed resistors** or as **variable resistors.**
Note All electrical components provide some resistance to the flow of electricity (e.g. filaments in bulbs are resistors that glow in a vacuum).

Connect up circuit **(5)** and place a low value resistor (100 Ω) in the circuit and then a high value resistor (10 kΩ). What is the difference?

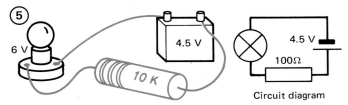

(a) By connecting up circuit **(6)** the bulb's brightness can be varied.
(b) Replace the bulb with a small motor or a buzzer. What happens?

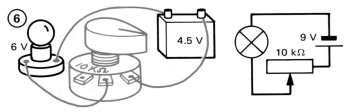

THE LIGHT DEPENDENT RESISTOR (LDR)
The resistance of an LDR varies depending on the amount of light landing on it.

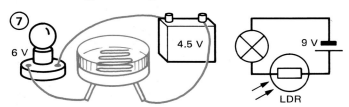

What happens when you cover the LDR up with your hand?

If more than one resistor or resistive component is connected up in a circuit it is important to realise that there are two basic ways of connecting the components – in **series** or in **parallel.**

CONNECTING RESISTORS IN SERIES
When resistors or resistive components (e.g. bulbs) are connected up in **series** the total resistance value can be found by **adding** up all the resistive values. This formula can be written down as follows:

$$\text{resistance} = R_1 + R_2 + R_3 \ldots$$
$$\text{(total)} \qquad \text{(resistor values)}$$

Connect up 3 bulbs in series as shown in diagram **(8)**. Is the brightness of the bulbs increased or decreased?

RESISTORS CONNECTED UP IN PARALLEL
If resistors or resistive components are connected up in parallel, the total resistance does *not* increase; in fact the total resistance is slightly less than the lowest value resistor used.

Connect up the three bulbs in parallel as shown in diagram **(9)**. If the bulbs are all the same value, they will all stay as bright as each other. Do yours?

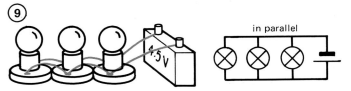

Ohm's law

George Ohm discovered that there is a relationship between **voltage, current and resistance**, which is usually written down as follows:

voltage (volts) = **current** (amps) × **resistance** (ohms)

By rearranging this formula we can find the resistance of a component:

$$\text{resistance (ohms)} = \frac{\text{voltage (volts)}}{\text{current (amps)}}$$

Question: Find the resistance of a 6 V bulb which consumes 0.1 A.

Switch types – as used on the opposite page.

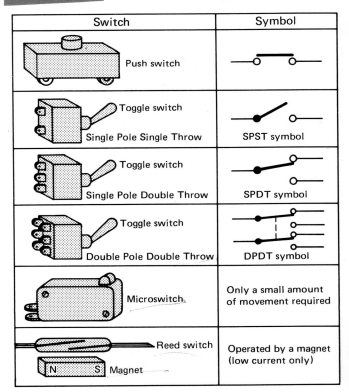

Switch	Symbol
Push switch	—o o—
Toggle switch — Single Pole Single Throw	SPST symbol
Toggle switch — Single Pole Double Throw	SPDT symbol
Toggle switch — Double Pole Double Throw	DPDT symbol
Microswitch	Only a small amount of movement required
Reed switch — Magnet	Operated by a magnet (low current only)

USING SWITCHES TO CONTROL BULBS, MOTORS ETC.

When assembling the circuits, notes should be made about each, indicating what each circuit could be used for in the 'real world'.

Circuit **(10)** is a simple on-and-off circuit controlling a bulb. A bell or motor can also be tried.

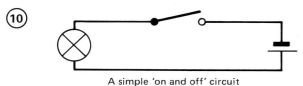

A simple 'on and off' circuit

The reed switch operates when a magnet is placed near it. Take care with reed switches because they are usually enclosed in a glass tube which can break easily.

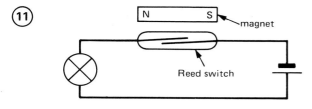

USING SWITCHES AS 'OR' OR 'AND' GATES

If more than one switch is used in a circuit they can be connected up in series to produce AND gates (switches), or in parallel to produce OR gates, as shown below:

Circuit **(12)** will only turn the bulb on if switch A *and* switch B are turned on (an AND gate).

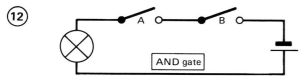

Question: Can you now make a 'burglar alarm' circuit using three switches *and* a bell?

Circuit **(13)** below will turn the bulb on if switch A *or* switch B is turned on (an OR gate).

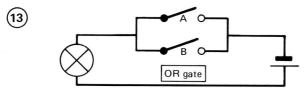

The rotary switch acts like a lot of separate OR switches. The circuit below uses a rotary switch to light up three bulbs which could be used outside the headmaster's door. The bulbs will then read *either* 'ENGAGED' *or* 'WAIT' *or* 'ENTER'.

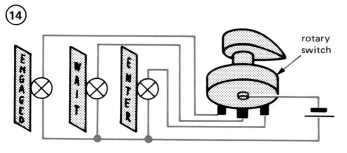

Diagram **(15)** is a useful reversing circuit for an electric motor (without the need to change the wires over). It uses a double-pole-double-throw (DPDT) switch as shown below.

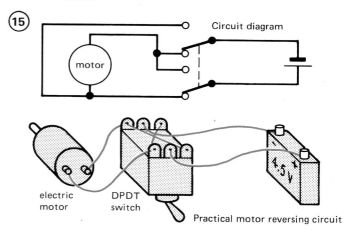

Practical motor reversing circuit

SIMPLE PROGRAMMING USING SWITCHES

It is reasonably easy to programme a sequence of events using switches and a cam. Microswitches with a lever attached are the easiest to turn 'on' and 'off' as required.

Try making circuit **(16)**. Construction kits can be used to support the cam and microswitch(es). The speed of the light flashing 'on' and 'off' is dependent on how fast the cam is turned and the number of lobes on the cam. Early washing machines used a similar system to control the water, heating, wash and spin cycles.

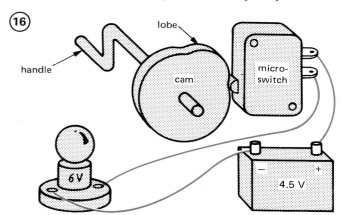

Disco lights

A disco effect can be obtained by three microswitches arranged in a similar way to diagram below. (Other ideas are on page 96.)

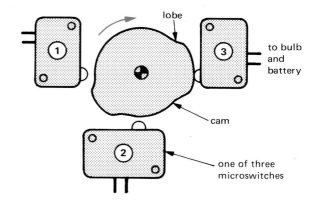

Magnets, electromagnets and relays

MAGNETS

Permanent types of magnets are made from special steels. The steel is magnetised and one end is called the **north pole** and the other end the **south pole.** Magnets have the following properties:

1 Unlike poles **attract** each other.
2 Like poles **repel** each other (push apart).
3 Either pole is attracted to steel.

Can you name four objects a magnet can pick up?

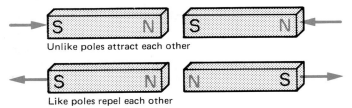

Unlike poles attract each other

Like poles repel each other

ELECTROMAGNETS

Electromagnets behave like magnets, but can be turned 'on' and 'off' at will: they are temporary magnets. A simple electromagnet can be made by winding enamelled copper wire round a soft iron rod. The more turns of wire used, the more powerful it will be.

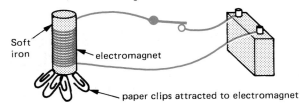

Soft iron

electromagnet

paper clips attracted to electromagnet

PRACTICAL USES FOR ELECTROMAGNETS

A bell is operated by an electromagnet.

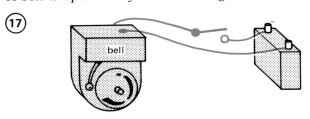

⑰

bell

Solenoid

A solenoid consists of a coil of wire wrapped round a plastic tube. When the electricity is turned 'on' the soft iron plunger is pulled into the tube.

⑱ plunger

to battery

Relays

A relay consists of switches which are turned 'on' and 'off' by an electromagnet. The outline of a relay is shown below. When a small electric current flows through the electromagnet an iron armature moves and the electric switch contacts are closed (or opened depending on the arrangement). They are often used to connect up two circuits using different voltages. This enables delicate components to be protected.

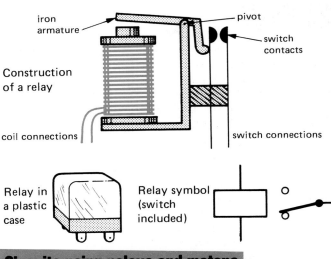

iron armature — pivot — switch contacts

Construction of a relay

coil connections — switch connections

Relay in a plastic case

Relay symbol (switch included)

Circuits using relays and motors

Note It is a good idea if these circuits are mounted on a vehicle similar to the one shown below (photo on page 88).

Circuit **(19)** is switched 'on' and 'off' by the 'reed switch' (the vehicle can then be stopped by the magnet).

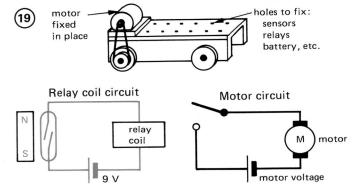

⑲ motor fixed in place — holes to fix: sensors relays battery, etc.

Relay coil circuit — relay coil — 9 V

Motor circuit — M motor — motor voltage

Circuit **(20)** is operated by a light beam. A torch can be used.

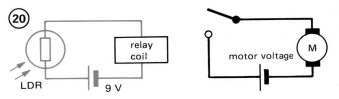

⑳ relay coil — LDR — 9 V — motor voltage — M

Circuit **(21)** shows a reversing circuit operated by one simple on/off switch. (Place a large capacitor, e.g. 5000 μF, across the relay coil to obtain a delay.)

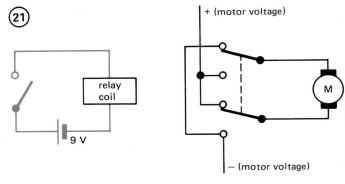

㉑ relay coil — 9 V

+ (motor voltage) — M — − (motor voltage)

ELECTRONICS

The study of electronics naturally follows on from the study of electrics. The next few pages describe the extra electronic components needed, in addition to those already explained in the electrics section. Then there follow the electronic circuits you can make (or which your teacher can demonstrate).

Note A Care needs to be taken if a circuit is to work first time. Do not connect the battery up until you and your teacher have double-checked the circuit.
Note B Success is more likely if a ready-made demonstration circuit can be referred to when problems arise.
Note C The components used here are reasonably easy to obtain, but if you are making a circuit copied from a magazine, ensure you can obtain *all* the parts needed.

Components and basic theory

— not already covered under Electrics and Electronics.

ELECTRONIC DIAGRAMS
Electronic diagrams are drawn
— using vertical and horizontal lines wherever possible,
— with joints indicated by a large dot,
— with 'crossed wires' (not touching) left without a dot.

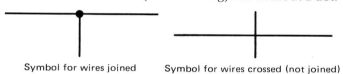

Symbol for wires joined   Symbol for wires crossed (not joined)

RESISTORS
Resistors have already been described in the electrics section. In Electronics you will probably need to read the resistor colour code illustrated below.

Resistor colour code

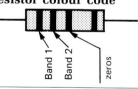

Colour	1	2	Zeros
Black	0	0	
Brown	1	1	0
Red	2	2	00
Orange	3	3	000
Yellow	4	4	0000
Green	5	5	00000
Blue	6	6	000000
Violet	7	7	0000000
Grey	8	8	00000000
White	9	9	000000000

Example: Find the value of this resistor.

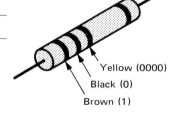

Yellow (0000)
Black (0)
Brown (1)

Answer:
Value = 100000 ohms
(or 100 kΩ)

Note The fourth band indicates how accurately it has been made, e.g.

gold band = accurate to ±5%,
silver band = accurate to ±10%.

Question:
What colours will be found on a 1 kΩ resistor?

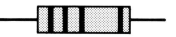

CAPACITORS
Capacitors store electrical energy and can be used to

— provide a time delay, or
— allow alternating current (a.c.) to pass through, but block direct current (d.c.), e.g. in audio amplifiers, or
— filter out unwanted signals, e.g. a car's suppressor.

There are two basic types of capacitor:

1 **Capacitors (non-electrolytic).**
2 **Electrolytic capacitors** which are used for large values of capacitance; they must be connected the right way round, i.e. + to + and − to −.

Capacitors are measured in farads, F, but in practical electronics we only use small fractions of a farad, such as a microfarad (written μF or mfd). The maximum voltage is also written on the capacitor as shown below.

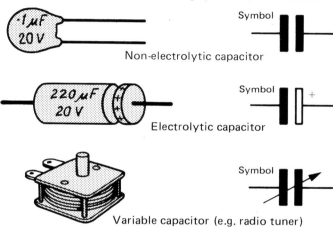

Symbol
Non-electrolytic capacitor

Symbol
Electrolytic capacitor

Symbol
Variable capacitor (e.g. radio tuner)

SEMICONDUCTORS
In electronics, **semiconductors** are used in the manufacture of diodes, transistors etc. They are materials that cannot normally conduct electricity but can be made to do so, i.e. materials that can be made to behave like **insulators** *or* **conductors**. The most common semiconducting material used is **silicon**.

DIODES
Diodes are made up from an 'N' (negative) type and a 'P' (positive) semiconductor joined together. They allow electricity to flow in one direction only (it is rather like an electrical one-way street). Some special diodes are available which emit light and are called light-emitting diodes (or LEDs). They are sometimes used instead of small coloured bulbs.

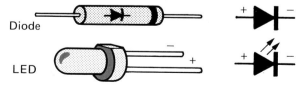

Diode

LED

TRANSISTORS
Transistors can be used to

— act as a fast electrical **switch**, or
— **amplify** electrical signals.

Transistors come in two basic types depending on how the semiconductor layers have been arranged, and are called 'NPN' type or 'PNP' type.

NPN type transistors are used throughout this book. The three connections to the transistor are called **base** (b), **collector** (c) and **emitter** (e).

Note Transistors are always viewed from below.

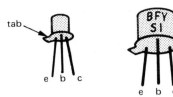
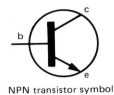

NPN transistor symbol

CHIPS (INTEGRATED CIRCUITS)
Chips are made out of a slice (or chip) of silicon. Within each chip is a complete **integrated circuit** containing transistors, resistors, diodes etc. **Microprocessors** used in computers are large chips that process information.

Note All semiconductor devices need to be connected up correctly to the battery.

The chip as bought in a package

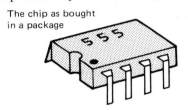

Chip symbol

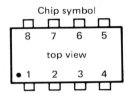

top view

Construction techniques

– for electronic circuits

There is a wide choice of techniques available, ranging from simple nails on a wooden board to mass-produced 'printed circuit' boards. In schools a system that is easy to check should be used, such as a **breadboard** circuit.

BREADBOARD CONSTRUCTION TECHNIQUES
With this method all the circuitry is assembled on one side of the board, making it easy to check against the circuit diagram.

Constructing a breadboard circuit
1 Draw the circuit diagram on a piece of paper and then tape it on to the breadboard to be used.
2 Lay the components to be used on the circuit diagram and check everything is correct.
3 Decide where you need the pins and then put them in place.
4 Solder the components in place (leaving the delicate components until last, such as transistors).
5 Add external fittings such as battery clips.

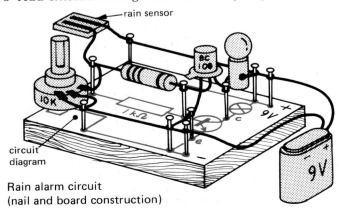

Rain alarm circuit
(nail and board construction)

The screw and screwcap construction method below is useful for simple circuits.

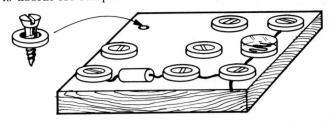

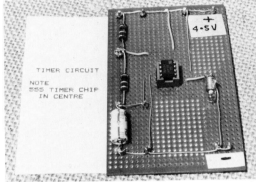

A 555 timer circuit mounted on a piece of perforated board.

Hints on soldering

- Clean the end of the soldering iron with a file, and then 'tin' it using multicore soft solder before starting.
- Use 'tin coated copper wire' for the circuit.
- Apply the soldering iron to the **opposite** side of the nail or pin as shown below. When the pin has heated up sufficiently, the solder flows round the pin to the soldering iron.

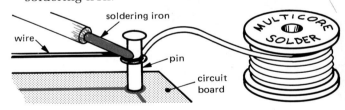

Potential dividers

– or voltage dividers

This is a cheap method of reducing the voltage using two resistors.

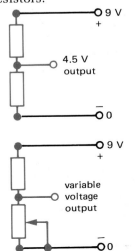

For example the output of the potential divider here is 4.5 volts although 9 volts is supplied from the battery.

By using a variable resistor as well, the output voltage can be varied.

Can you spot where the **potential dividers** are on the next page.

Electronic circuits to make

Note For ease of construction the circuit diagrams shown should be doubled in size (i.e. lengths doubled).

The electronic circuits on this page marked **E1** to **E4** can be used for a wide variety of projects, such as a **rain alarm**, a **burglar alarm**, a **fire alarm**, all of which can operate bulbs or motors. Also included is a **flashing-light** circuit and a **siren** (which can be converted into an organ).

SENSITIVE SWITCHING CIRCUITS

The circuit below can be 'pre-set' by adjusting the variable resistor. If the 4.7 kΩ resistor (in red) is removed and replaced by

- an **LDR**, the circuit will respond to changes in the light levels.
- a **thermistor**, the circuit will respond to changes in temperature (use a match to heat it up).
- a **water sensor**, the circuit will respond if the sensor is moist.

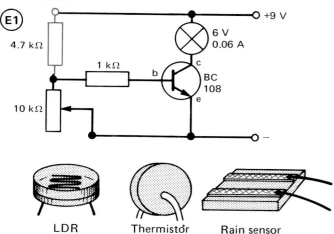

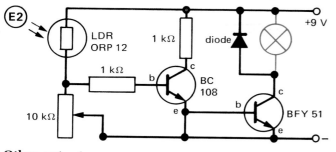

LDR   Thermistor   Rain sensor

AN EVEN MORE SENSITIVE SWITCHING CIRCUIT

The circuit below has an extra transistor stage for extra sensitivity. The diode gives protection to the second transistor when operating a motor or a relay.

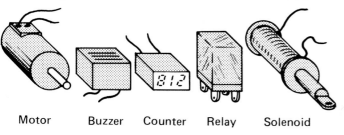

Other outputs

The bulb (in red) can be replaced by any of the components below.
Note They must all be suitable for 5 to 9 volt use.

Motor   Buzzer   Counter   Relay   Solenoid

USING A RELAY TO SWITCH ON LARGER MOTORS ETC.

Large motors can be operated by circuit **E2** if it is connected up via a relay (a separate power supply will be needed for the motor).

A FLASHING LIGHT CIRCUIT (ASTABLE MULTI-VIBRATOR)

When this circuit is turned on the bulbs flash 'on' and 'off' alternately. The rate of flashing is determined by the values of the resistors and capacitors (in red).

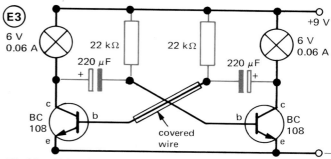

Flashing light circuit

Things you can try

1 Place various capacitors across those already in place.
2 Use variable resistors instead of the two fixed resistors.
3 Replace one of the bulbs with a 1 kΩ resistor (if only one bulb is needed).

SIREN

(This circuit can also be converted into an organ, see bottom of the page.)

The **siren circuit** is in principle the same as the **flashing light circuit** except that the capacitors have lower values, so that the circuit switches 'on' and 'off' much faster and drives a speaker instead of the bulbs.

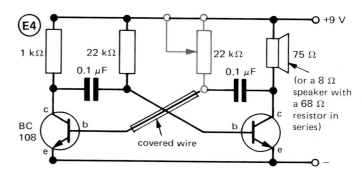

ORGAN

To make an eight-note organ, the following circuit is added in place of the 22 kΩ variable resistor (in red).

To tune the organ, the presets are adjusted while the probe is touching the appropriate key.

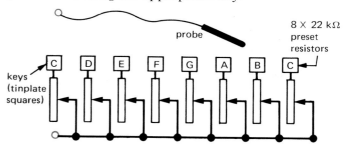

Projects to make

Various projects are shown on this and the next two pages. The circuit diagrams on the last few pages can also be used for project ideas.

Note Before making an expensive electric or electronic project, make sure it does what you want it to do, e.g. will the circuit be powerful or bright enough?

MAGNETIC TOYS
(Magnets in red.)

IDEAS

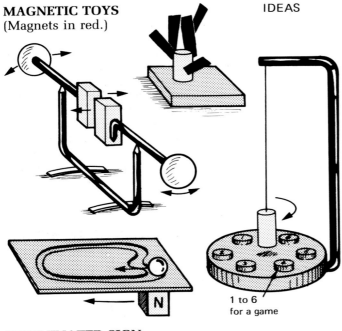

1 to 6
for a game

ILLUMINATED SIGN

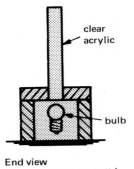

clear acrylic

bulb

scratched acrylic glows

End view
(cut away to show bulb)

ROBOT MASK
(The eyes light up.)

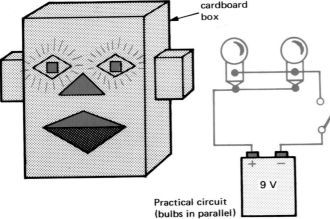

cardboard box

Practical circuit
(bulbs in parallel)

9 V

'ROUND THE POLE' HOVERCRAFT

The hovercraft flies round the central pole. One propeller pushes the craft (fast) round the pole, while the other lifts it from the floor.

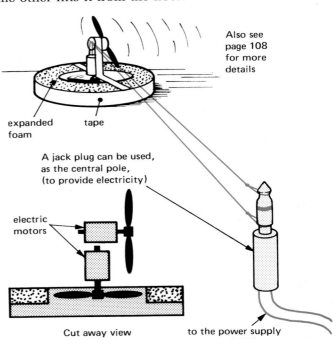

Also see page 108 for more details

expanded foam

tape

A jack plug can be used, as the central pole, (to provide electricity)

electric motors

Cut away view

to the power supply

FLASHING LIGHT

The model gives a disco or traffic light effect. It can be motorised.

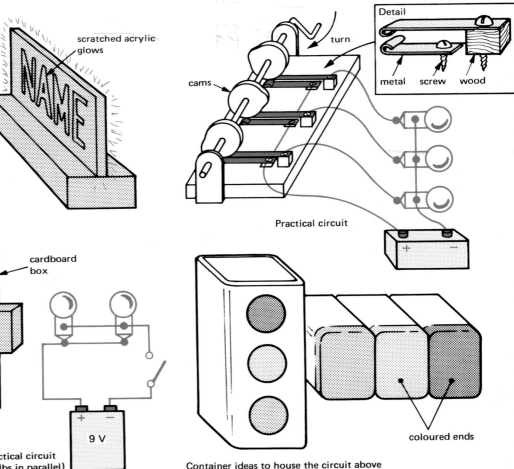

Detail

metal   screw   wood

turn

cams

Practical circuit

coloured ends

Container ideas to house the circuit above

WIND SPEED INDICATOR (ANEMOMETER)

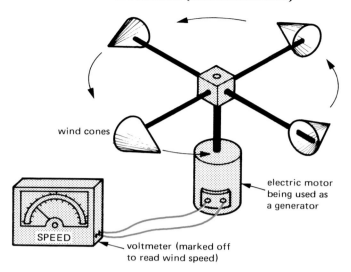

wind cones

electric motor being used as a generator

SPEED

voltmeter (marked off to read wind speed)

FUSE TESTER

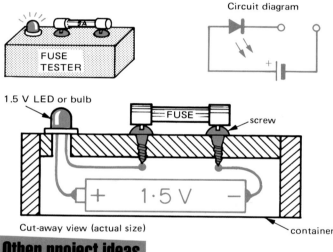

Circuit diagram

FUSE TESTER

1.5 V LED or bulb

FUSE

screw

+ 1·5 V −

Cut-away view (actual size)

container

Other project ideas

Burglar alarm system – for doors, windows, computers etc.

An illuminated sign (or fun box) A bulb inside a container illuminates the sign.

Soil moisture tester Circuit **E2** can be adapted to do this (wire probes replacing the LDR).

A large seven-segment number display Seven bulbs can be illuminated from behind a display board and controlled by seven switches.

A robot (or mask) Make it out of cheap materials, then add flashing lights etc.

A reaction timer Devise a method of measuring the reaction time of a person using an electric motor and a piece of string.

Putting on a show Control the circuits already made (at least three) using microswitches and a cam.

Model railways A lot of scope here!

An expanded polystyrene cutter Resistance wire, a frame support and a largish battery are needed.

Police vehicle Add siren and flashing light on top of a model car.

Questions and exercises — electrics and electronics

1 List 12 products that use electricity; indicate which can be operated by a battery and which from the 'mains'.
2 Draw a game that can make use of one or two magnets (explain how it is to be used).
3 (a) What do the following letters stand for: V, I, A?
(b) Draw a typical fixed resistor and capacitor symbol, then write down the units we measure them in.
4 Draw three different kinds of switches and then write a sentence giving a typical application for each.
5 (a) Draw the symbols that represent the following: resistor, capacitor, bulb, speaker, LDR and a motor.
(b) Draw the symbols for a diode and an 'NPN' transistor. Name the connections to the transistor.
6 How could you control three motors 'on' then 'off' in turn, using switches and a cam? Draw your answer.
7 Copy the flashing light diagram on page 95 as neatly as possible, then explain what practical use it could have.

COMMON ELECTRIC AND ELECTRONIC SYMBOLS

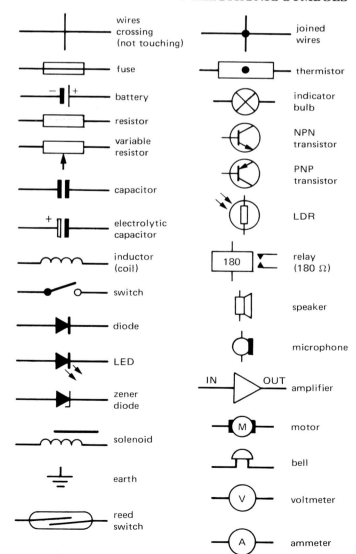

wires crossing (not touching)

joined wires

fuse

thermistor

battery

indicator bulb

resistor

NPN transistor

variable resistor

PNP transistor

capacitor

LDR

electrolytic capacitor

relay (180 Ω)

inductor (coil)

switch

speaker

diode

microphone

LED

amplifier

zener diode

motor

solenoid

bell

earth

voltmeter

reed switch

ammeter

COMPUTERS IN CDT

Computers are becoming increasingly important in our lives because of their increased versatility and reliability. This short section shows a few of the ways in which a computer can be used in CDT. The control of robots is an obvious example but computers can also be used in other ways such as:

- **producing typed text for use in a report,**
- **as a teaching aid using CDT teaching programs,**
- **as a graphic designer to help with your drawings and design work etc.**

Examples are shown at the bottom of the page opposite.

Computers are essentially machines for doing arithmetic very fast. Programs are needed to instruct the computer to carry out these calculations in the way required.

It is essential that well written programs are used because either bad programs will produce rubbish or the computer will indicate that it cannot cope. The earliest computers were mechanical and used mainly as adding machines. In the 1940s computers using electric valves were used but they were not very powerful. Now, thanks to the 'micro-chip' we have very powerful computers with increasingly large amounts of memory that ordinary people can afford.

Nearly all the computers used nowadays are **binary computers.** This means they do their very fast calculations in binary arithmetic counting in one's and zero's (or 'pulse' or 'no pulse' of electricity).

A computer has three main stages: the **input** stage, the **central processing** stage and the **output** stage. The diagrams below show various **input** and **output** methods that can be used.

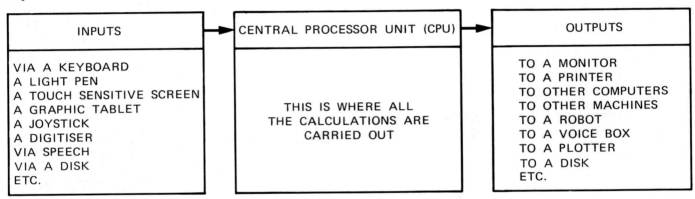

INPUTS	CENTRAL PROCESSOR UNIT (CPU)	OUTPUTS
VIA A KEYBOARD A LIGHT PEN A TOUCH SENSITIVE SCREEN A GRAPHIC TABLET A JOYSTICK A DIGITISER VIA SPEECH VIA A DISK ETC.	THIS IS WHERE ALL THE CALCULATIONS ARE CARRIED OUT	TO A MONITOR TO A PRINTER TO OTHER COMPUTERS TO OTHER MACHINES TO A ROBOT TO A VOICE BOX TO A PLOTTER TO A DISK ETC.

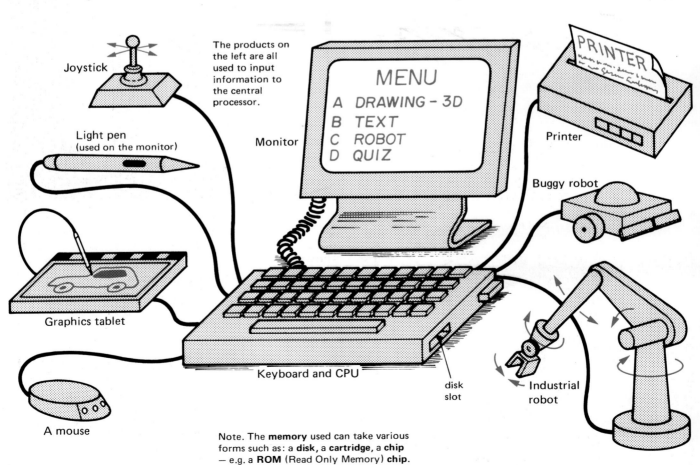

Joystick

Light pen
(used on the monitor)

The products on the left are all used to input information to the central processor.

Monitor

MENU
A DRAWING – 3D
B TEXT
C ROBOT
D QUIZ

PRINTER

Printer

Graphics tablet

Buggy robot

A mouse

Keyboard and CPU

disk slot

Industrial robot

Note. The **memory** used can take various forms such as: a **disk**, a **cartridge**, a **chip** — e.g. a **ROM** (Read Only Memory) **chip**.

Interfaces

Interfaces allow various input or output devices to be safely linked to the **central processor unit.** There are two main kinds:

I The kind that protects the computer from high voltages and high electrical current.

A relay is often used for this. A 'buggy robot' would need this kind of interface.

*II The **interface** that converts **analogue** signals into suitable **digital** signals, or vice versa*

A 'heat sensor' producing an analogue output (i.e. different voltages at different temperatures) needs this kind of interface to convert the analogue signals into digital signals. (Some computers have these already built in with connections to an 'analogue port'.)

The following is an example of a school-made interface used to drive a simple 'buggy robot'. It is driven and steered by two electric motors.

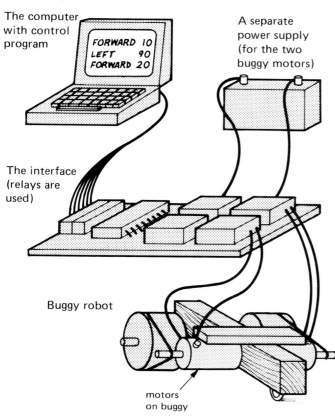

The computer with control program

FORWARD 10
LEFT 90
FORWARD 20

A separate power supply (for the two buggy motors)

The interface (relays are used)

Buggy robot

motors on buggy

Three uses for computers

1 A computer-controlled crane used to move a toy (an interface is needed like the example above).

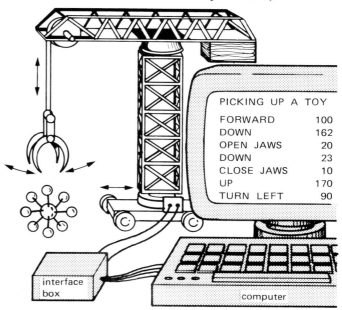

PICKING UP A TOY

FORWARD	100
DOWN	162
OPEN JAWS	20
DOWN	23
CLOSE JAWS	10
UP	170
TURN LEFT	90

interface box

computer

2 An example of **computer aided design** (CAD). It was drawn by a 12-year-old using a simple program.

C.A.D.

TV

3 An example of computer 'print-out' to be glued on a design folder, produced on the school computer with a dot matrix printer. Various tones can be produced as shown.

CRAFT DESIGN AND TECHNOLOGY BY S. DUNN

A simple, easy-to-make computer controlled buggy

Note It can also be controlled manually with switches.

This **buggy** can be made very easily out of two cheap electric motors, two containers, elastic bands, metal rod for the shafts, a castor for the rear and a main frame as shown below. (For extra help with construction see page 85.) An **interface** is needed to protect the computer; your teacher will probably have one you can borrow. The large gear ratio required is achieved by driving directly from the electric drive shaft to the large diameter wheels.

THINGS TO TRY

1 Control the buggy directly with the computer keys (ask your teacher for the program required).
2 Have a competition to see who can steer it round a course in the quickest time.
3 Use a program (or write your own) that will allow you to repeat the buggy's path over and over again.
4 Add another motor to do something else, e.g. 'grab arm'.
5 Drill a hole in between the two wheels, then place a pen in it so that the buggy can make drawings as it travels along.

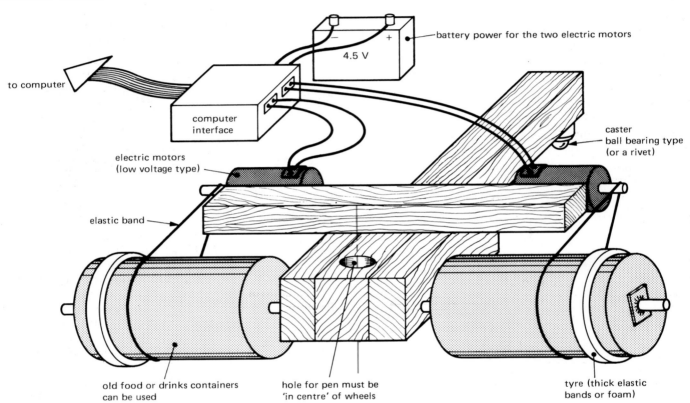

battery power for the two electric motors

4.5 V

to computer

computer interface

caster
ball bearing type
(or a rivet)

electric motors
(low voltage type)

elastic band

old food or drinks containers
can be used

hole for pen must be
'in centre' of wheels

tyre (thick elastic
bands or foam)

TESTING IT MANUALLY

Before connecting the 'buggy' up to the computer it can be tested manually by controlling it with switches as shown below. If long wires are used it can be made to go round mazes etc.

HOW THIS KIND OF BUGGY STEERS

If both wheels turn forwards, the buggy moves straight ahead. When only one wheel turns, the buggy turns round pivoting on the stationary wheel. If both wheels turn but in opposite directions, the buggy will turn 'on the spot' (this is the method used when the buggy draws).

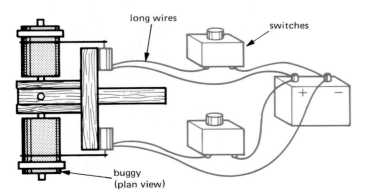

long wires

switches

buggy
(plan view)

Wiring diagram for manual control

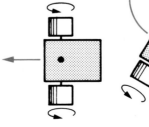

forward

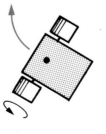

one wheel turning

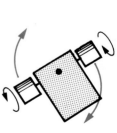

both wheels turning
but in opposite
directions

CONTROL WITH COMPUTERS COURSE

This course uses BBC BASIC.

When a special **control interface** is connected to the **user port** (INPUT/OUTPUT port) of the computer, it can be used to control: electric motors, light bulbs, solenoids etc.

Projects that can be controlled include: robots, buggies, model traffic lights, model houses with bulbs etc.

The exercises and programs given form a simple **COURSE IN CONTROL WITH COMPUTERS**. The long programs are best recorded on disk (your teacher may have done this).

Notes

(a) It is assumed that the interface you use has indicator lights.

(b) If a computer enthusiast starts this course first, there will be another person besides the teacher to ask for help.

(c) The end of this section explains how to **change, edit** and **load** a program from a disk.

COMPUTER MATHS (adding up in binary)

All digital computers use **binary numbers** to work; a binary number can only be a '0' or '1' (i.e. 'ON' or 'OFF'). Three examples are given showing how to convert to a normal decimal number into binary.

```
DECIMAL TO BINARY EXAMPLES

              8 4 2 1   value of columns
1 in binary is  0 0 0 1
3 in binary is  0 0 1 1  (one 2 and one 1 = 3)
12 in binary is 1 1 0 0  (one 8 and one 4 = 12)
```

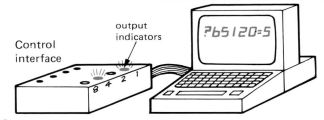

1 CONTROLLING THE OUTPUTS YOU WANT

Type in the following codes:

?65122=255 — This **'sets up'** the user port ready for use.
The rest of the codes are all **?65120=**

?65120=1 — This turns the **first** output on.

?65120=2 — This turns the **second** output on.

?65120=3 — **First** and **second** output on (i.e. 2 + 1 in binary).

?65120=9 — **Fourth** and **first** output on (i.e. 8 + 1 in binary).

```
TO CHANGE OR EDIT A PROGRAM

• The DELETE key is used to rub out (delete) any
  typing errors you make.

• New lines of program are typed in; then press
  RETURN. This will automatically replace any
  existing numbered line; to check, type LIST
  and press RETURN.

• If the COPY key is pressed it will copy text that
  the cursor is under.
```

Questions

What **code** and **number** is needed to: (a) turn 'ON' **all** the outputs, (b) turn 'ON' the **two centre** outputs?

2 TO CONTROL A SIMPLE BUGGY
(using two d.c. motors)

Connect the buggy up, then type in the following:

?65122=255 This sets up the user port.
Then type in: ?65120=5 Observe which motors work.
Then type in: ?65120=X X = any number between 1 and 15

Experiment with the values of X, then complete the following:

To make the buggy go **forwards** ?65120=
To make the buggy go **backwards** ?65120=
To make the buggy go **left** ?65120=
To make the buggy go **right** ?65120=
To make the buggy **stop** ?65120=

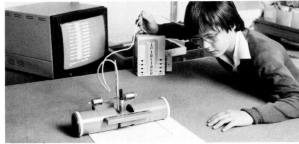

School-made buggy, made from drink containers, two motors and wood. Note the use of the interface.

3 WRITING YOUR FIRST CONTROL PROGRAM
To control bulbs, buggies, cranes etc.

Programs longer than one line require a method of **ordering** (i.e. numbering in steps of ten). Type in the program below, then RUN it. It can be as long as you like. To alter the time each output is 'ON', vary the 5000 number (5000 represents 5 seconds).

```
10 ?65122=255            'Sets up' the user port.
20 ?65120=3              First and second output ON.
30 FOR D=1 TO 5000:NEXT D   5 second delay.
40 ?65120=4              Third output on.
50 FOR D=1 TO 5000:NEXT D   5 second delay.
60.......etc             Continue if you want.
```

When ready, press the RETURN key; type RUN, then press RETURN again. To make it continuously repeat, add this line: 500 GOTO 20

A LEGO® interface being used to control a LEGO model made from the LEGO Technic Control Set 1090.

4 A VERSATILE CONTROL PROGRAM
(that is easy to use)

This program has many possibilities and is reasonably easy to use because all the information needed is contained in DATA statements at the end (lines 310 to 340). Each of the DATA statement lines contains two bits of information:

1 The outputs to be turned ON (in **binary** code).
2 The time the output is on in seconds × 100, i.e. 200 = 2 seconds.

LOAD and RUN the program, then change the first DATA statement by typing 310 DATA1,800. This turns on OUTPUT '1' for **8 seconds**, when the program is RUN again. The other DATA statements can be altered, or added to, in the same way.

```
 10 REM   *CALLED    "CONTROL"*
 20 ?65122=255
 30 READA
 40 IFA=-1 THEN 270
 50 IFA=0  PRINT"0000 OUTPUT"
 60 IFA=1  PRINT"0001 OUTPUT"
 70 IFA=2  PRINT"0010 OUTPUT"
 80 IFA=3  PRINT"0011 OUTPUT"
 90 IFA=4  PRINT"0100 OUTPUT"
100 IFA=5  PRINT"0101 OUTPUT"
110 IFA=6  PRINT"0110 OUTPUT"
120 IFA=7  PRINT"0111 OUTPUT"
130 IFA=8  PRINT"1000 OUTPUT"
140 IFA=9  PRINT"1001 OUTPUT"
150 IFA=10 PRINT"1010 OUTPUT"
160 IFA=11 PRINT"1011 OUTPUT"
170 IFA=12 PRINT"1100 OUTPUT"
180 IFA=13 PRINT"1101 OUTPUT"
190 IFA=14 PRINT"1110 OUTPUT"
200 IFA=15 PRINT"1111 OUTPUT"
210 READB
220 PRINT"     FOR ";B/100" SECONDS"
230 ?65120=A
240 D=TIME+B
250 REPEATUNTILTIME=D
260 GOTO 30
270 ?65120=0
280 PRINT "******** END *********"
290 PRINT "   TO REPEAT TYPE 'RUN'"
300 PRINT "   THEN PRESS   'RETURN'"
310 DATA9,200
320 DATA3,200
330 DATA6,200
340 DATA12,100
1000 DATA-1
```

In order to make this program repeat by itself, the following lines need to be typed in. (They will automatically go to the correct place in the program when RUN.)

```
270 RESTORE 310
275 GOTO 30
1000 DATA-1,-1
```

LOADING A PROGRAM FROM DISK
- Switch computer ON, then insert **disk** into DISK DRIVE.
- Type LOAD " ". Then press RETURN key (program name goes in between the two " " marks, e.g. LOAD "BUGGY".
- Type RUN. Then press RETURN key.

5 A USER-FRIENDLY BUGGY CONTROL PROGRAM

No prior knowledge of computers is needed to operate this program. All you have to do is select the **direction** and the **time** for each movement of the buggy.

Note If the wiring of the buggy makes it move in a different direction from that indicated in the program, lines 60 and 70 can be edited using the values found in section 2 on page 101.

See if you can make the buggy move in a 300 mm square. Note that the memory is lost when the computer is turned off.

```
 10 REM *CALLED "BUGGY"
 20 ?65122=255
 30 DIM M(50)
 40 DIM R(50)
 50 FOR N=1 TO 50
 60 PRINT"SELECT 'NUMBER' + <RETURN>"
 70 PRINT" 5=RIGHT        10=LEFT"
 80 PRINT" 3=BACKWARD     12=FORWARD"
 90 PRINT" O=PAUSE        -1=TO FINISH"
100 INPUT M(N)
110 IF M(N)=-1 THEN 150
120PRINT"TYPE TIME IN 1/10TH SECONDS"
130 INPUT R(N)
140 NEXT N
150 PRINT" TO WORK PRESS SPACE BAR"
160 G=GET
170 FOR N=1 TO 50
180 ?65120=M(N)
190 IF M(N)=-1 THEN 220
200T=TIME+R(N)*10:REPEAT UNTIL TIME=T
210 NEXT N
220 ?65120=0
230 PRINT"**<SPACE BAR> TO REPEAT **"
240 GOTO 160
```

Interface and crane from Pilot One, Bedford, controlled from the computer.

Technical notes for information only

Other languages that are based on LOGO may be easier for young children. The **Pilot Digital Interface** is used by the author; only some of its capabilities are shown. **Input sensors** such as switches, LDRs, thermistors etc. can also be used but are not described here.

ENERGY

This section gives some basic theory and then provides various project ideas and competition ideas which you can try. Questions are at the end.

The terms used in this section (such as work and power) have precise meanings and must not be confused with the same words used in other ways.

Note Energy or power requirements need to be considered in most technological projects.

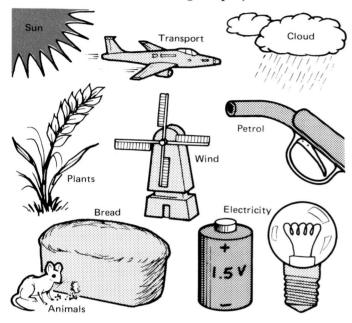

Kinds of energy

Nearly all forms of energy came originally (and are still coming) from the sun. A lot of the sun's energy is used by plants. The plants in turn are either eaten by animals and humans or left to decay. After thousands of years some of the dead matter will have been converted into coal and oil, which can in turn be used to heat a home, etc.

Energy is described as **the capacity to do work**. Energy comes in various forms; the commonly used ones are described below.

POTENTIAL ENERGY (STORED ENERGY)

Potential energy has the capacity to do work. For example a rock on the edge of a cliff has the potential to do work (e.g. knock a wall down) due to its postion. The higher the cliff, the more potential energy the rock is said to have. Other examples of potential energy are a stretched elastic band and a compressed spring.

Examples of potential energy

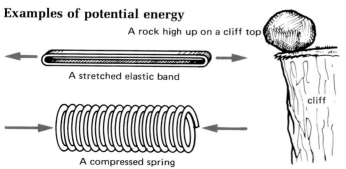

A rock high up on a cliff top

A stretched elastic band

A compressed spring

KINETIC ENERGY (MOVING ENERGY)

When an object moves it is said to have **kinetic energy**. Both a person running and a rock falling from a cliff are moving and therefore have kinetic energy. Other examples include the elastic band and the spring when they are released as shown below.

Note **Potential energy** can be converted to **kinetic energy**. When the objects come to rest they possess no energy.

Examples of kinetic energy

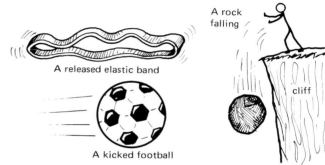

A released elastic band

A kicked football

A rock falling

cliff

CHEMICAL ENERGY

This is the energy stored in a chemical form. Examples include coal and oil which release their energy when burnt. Electric batteries also rely on chemical change to work.

NUCLEAR POWER

This is the energy available when certain elements (e.g. uranium) are made to split up and release heat. There are some radiation risks with this kind of energy so special precautions are needed.

NATURAL ENERGY SOURCES

These include the **sun, wind** and **water** power to provide heat, electricity, etc. These forms of energy are not usually as convenient to use as some of the other sources such as petrol, which can be stored cheaply until required. **Solar power** is being used more and more for heating water. It is a good method for heating swimming pools. **Wind** varies, making it difficult to match power requirements. **Water** is probably the easiest to store (in a reservoir), but a lot of water is needed for a given amount of power. **Wave** and **geothermal power** are two methods that are possibilities for the future.

Energy cannot be created or destroyed, but it can change its form.

This statement is called the principle of **conservation of energy**. To illustrate this, water energy can turn a turbine and produce electrical energy which in turn can be converted into heat energy by an electric heater; this heat could toast a piece of bread, a person can eat the toast and then cycle a bike, etc.

Force

Force is measured in **newtons**, N, named after Isaac Newton.

Note To convert weight in kilograms to newtons, use the following conversion:

$1 \text{ kg} = 9.81 \text{ N}$ (use 10 N for rough approximations).

This conversion is only true on earth.

Energy calculations

WORK DONE

In technology **work done** (or **work**) equals force × distance:

> **work done = force × distance**

The unit of **work** is the **newton metre** (or **joule**).
Force is measured in **newtons** and the **distance** is measured in **metres**.

Example: How much work is done if a rock weighing 100 newtons is lifted up through 4 metres?

Answer Work done = 100 N × 4 m
             = 400 N m (or 400 J)

POWER

This is the **rate** (speed) **of doing work** and is measured in **watts**, W. It is usually expressed as follows:

> **power (W) = $\dfrac{\text{work done (newton metres or joules)}}{\text{time taken (seconds)}}$**

Example calculation

How much power does the forklift truck need to lift 1000 newtons up through 2 metres in 5 seconds?

Answer

Power = $\dfrac{\text{work done}}{\text{time}}$

      = $\dfrac{1000 \text{ N} \times 2 \text{ m}}{5 \text{ s}}$

      = $\dfrac{2000}{5}$

Power = 400 watts.

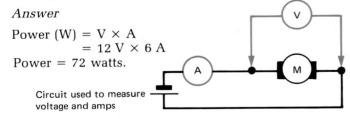

Forklift truck

1000 N

2 metres

MEASURING ELECTRICAL POWER

Electrical power can be measured directly using a **voltmeter** and an **ammeter**. The readings are then recorded and used in the following formula:

> **power (W) = voltage (V) × current (A)**

Example calculation

How much **power** does an electric motor use, given that the ammeter reading is 6 amps and the voltmeter reading is 12 volts?

Answer

Power (W) = V × A
          = 12 V × 6 A
Power = 72 watts.

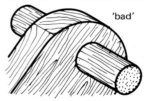

Circuit used to measure
voltage and amps

PAYING FOR ELECTRICITY

Mains electricity is paid for by the **unit**.

> **one unit = 1000 watts for one hour**

If a 2 kW heater is turned on for 4 hours it will have consumed 8 kilowatt hours or **8 units**.

EFFICIENCY

No machine is 100% efficient. If it were it would have achieved perpetual motion which has never been done; there are always unwanted losses, e.g. efficiency for an electric fire is about 98%, 85% for electric motors, 35% for a diesel engine and 6% for an early steam train engine.

Efficiency is always expressed as a percentage and is calculated as follows:

> **Efficiency (in %) = $\dfrac{\text{work out (useful)} \times 100\%}{\text{work input}}$**

Example calculation

A small 6 volt electric motor is supplied with 2 watts of power. The output at the shaft is 1.6 watts. What is the electric motor's efficiency?

Answer

Efficiency (%) = $\dfrac{\text{work out} \times 100\%}{\text{work in}}$

             = $\dfrac{1.6 \text{ watts} \times 100\%}{2 \text{ watts}}$

Efficiency = 80%

The other 20% is lost mainly as heat.

Making your project more efficient

Some project work is so inefficient that it hardly works. Below are a few tips to help you make the following reasonably efficient: 1 bearings, 2 gearing systems, and 3 wheels (for vehicles etc.).

1 BEARINGS

Two **simple plain bearings** are shown below.
The **'bad' plain bearing** is made out of high friction material (e.g. wood) and the shaft has too large a diameter. Large diameter shafts are more difficult to turn than smaller diameter shafts.

'bad'   'good'

Plain bearings

The **'good' plain bearing** uses lower friction materials (e.g. steel, acrylic, brass) and the diameter is kept as small as possible. Most bearings benefit from lubrication.

A **pivot bearing** is reasonably efficient but is only suitable for light loads.

Ball bearings are the most efficient bearings commonly used but are rather expensive for small school projects.

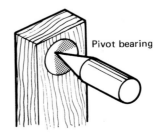

Pivot bearing

Ball bearing

2 GEARING

Gearing 'up' or 'down' can cause a large loss of energy. It is best to select, if possible, a power source that avoids the need for a lot of gearing. Some electric motors have their own gearboxes which save the need to make a separate gear system. If gearing is unavoidable, use a method with the least number of moving parts (i.e. only use two gears if they can achieve the same effect as four).

3 WHEELS

Large wheels roll along more easily than small wheels. Large wheels also have the effect of gearing up a powered model. This alters its speed and efficiency. Soft tyres are sometimes needed to obtain grip; they do not make the wheels roll more easily. Can you explain why cars need rubber tyres but trains do not?

To compare the effect of different wheels and shafts, test vehicles can be rolled down a standard slope to see how far they go (the best will go the furthest).

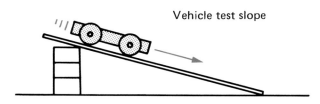

Vehicle test slope

How energy escapes from houses

When heating your house, what you are really doing is replacing the heat already lost through the wall, windows, the floor and the roof. Below are two houses: one has no extra insulation, the other has extra roof insulation, cavity wall insulation, double glazing and draught proofing. The result is that the people living in the uninsulated house pay *twice* as much for their heating to maintain the *same* temperature.

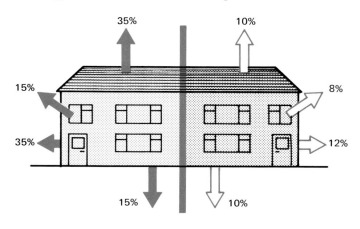

Uninsulated house   Insulated

Heat escapes in three main ways:

– by **conduction** (heat travels through the materials).
– by **convection** (heat carried away by the movement of the air).
– by **radiation**.

Note Vacuum flasks have been specially designed to reduce these three heat losses to a minimum.

PROJECT IDEAS

Power from the sun and wind

Things to consider

- The variations in wind and sun.
- Where will it be used?
- What will the energy be used for?
- What will happen in a storm?
- Will it be dangerous?

SOLAR STILL

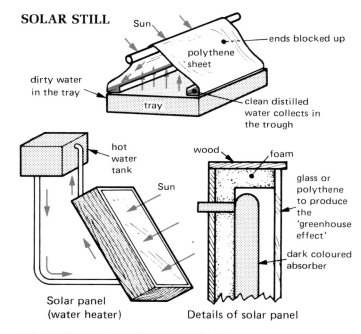

Solar panel (water heater)   Details of solar panel

HARNESSING ELECTRICITY FROM THE WIND

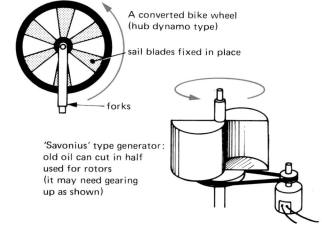

PROBLEM

Make a turbine (propeller) blade which, when attached to the generator and blown round, will light a bulb. (A vacuum cleaner on 'blow' can be used).

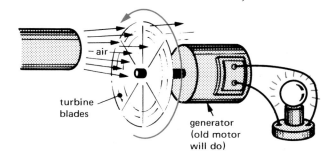

PROJECT IDEAS (CONTINUED)

Rubber powered vehicles

Sometimes competitions are held based on elastic power to drive a vehicle. The vehicle may be required to

— travel the furthest distance (a light, high-geared vehicle needed),
— travel the fastest,
— climb something.

Investigation questions

How can friction be reduced in your vehicle?
How will it be wound up?
Do you need good wheel grip?
Will it need to be geared up or down?
What wheel types should be used?
Does the vehicle have to be lightweight?
How can the elastic band be used? (wound, twisted, stretched?)
What surface will the vehicle be used on?

Vehicle forms can vary a great deal. Two examples are shown below.

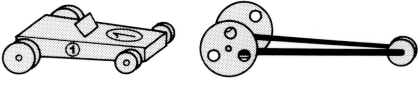

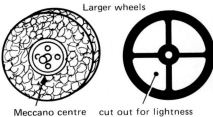

Wheel types

Meccano

Plywood or acrylic

Larger wheels

Meccano centre

cut out for lightness

Update of the 'cotton reel' vehicle

twisted elastic band

drinks container

elastic band

elastic band

weight

turn wheel to wind up

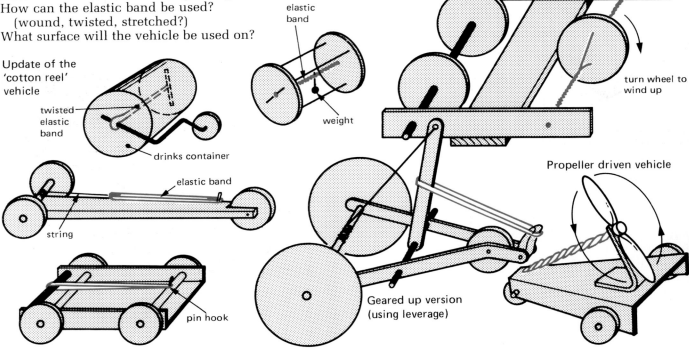

string

pin hook

Geared up version (using leverage)

Propeller driven vehicle

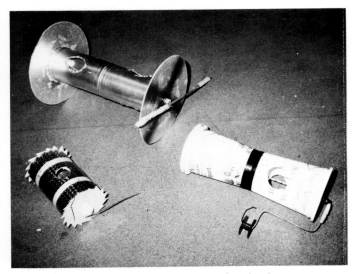

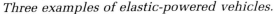

Three examples of elastic-powered vehicles.

Another elastic-powered vehicle made from a Fischertechnik kit. Note the gearing up method using leverage.

'Table tennis ball'-throwing competition

Design and make a device to throw a table tennis ball into a bucket a distance away decided by the teacher. Problems include: (a) firing it straight, (b) obtaining the same distance each throw, (c) holding mechanism still when 'firing'.

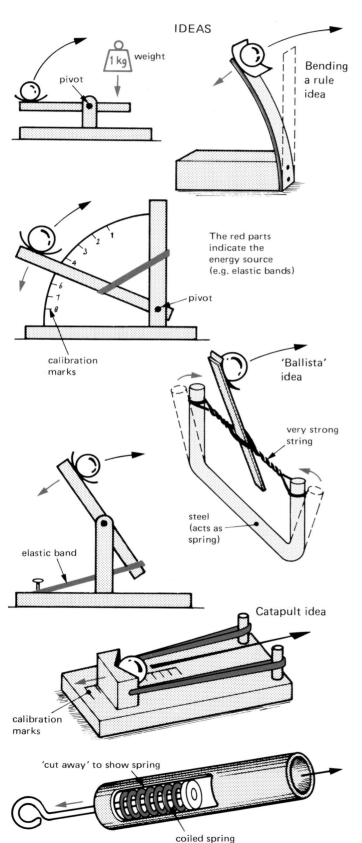

IDEAS

weight

pivot

Bending a rule idea

The red parts indicate the energy source (e.g. elastic bands)

pivot

calibration marks

'Ballista' idea

very strong string

steel (acts as spring)

elastic band

Catapult idea

calibration marks

'cut away' to show spring

coiled spring

Other energy-based project ideas

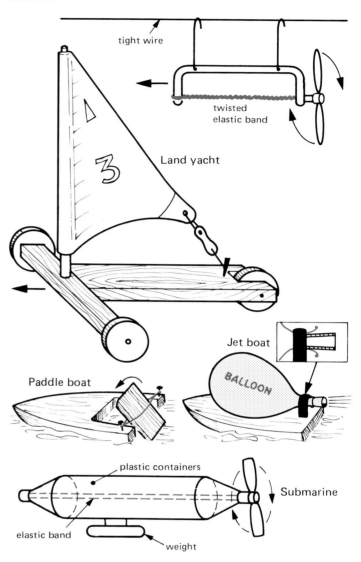

tight wire

twisted elastic band

Land yacht

Jet boat

Paddle boat

BALLOON

plastic containers

Submarine

elastic band

weight

Questions

1 Collect at least two advertisements that are trying to sell energy conservation products, e.g. double glazing, wall insulation, roof insulation etc.
2 Ask your parents what sources of energy are used for: heating your house, cooking. Find out how much your last electricity bill was.
3 How much power in **watts** is used by your: electric kettle, largest light bulb, television, radio? The answers should be printed on the product.
4 A girl using a pulley lifts a 50 N load up through a distance of 20 metres. How much **work** did she do? (Ignore pulley friction.)
5 A boy lifts 10 kg up through a distance of 20 metres. How much **work** did he do?
   Note First convert the kilograms into newtons).
6 How much **power** in **watts** did Tom produce when he lifted a 5 kg load a distance of 20 metres upwards in 40 seconds? (Convert kg into newtons.)
7 What **power** did an electric motor use when it ran off a 12 volt supply and the ammeter reading was 0.8 amps?

OTHER POPULAR PROJECTS

OUTDOOR KITES

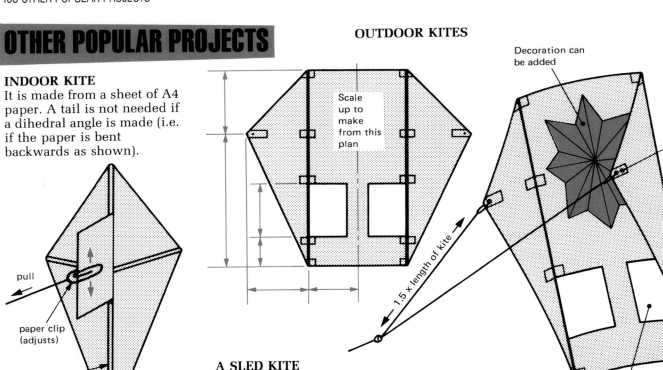

INDOOR KITE

It is made from a sheet of A4 paper. A tail is not needed if a dihedral angle is made (i.e. if the paper is bent backwards as shown).

pull

paper clip (adjusts)

straw

A SLED KITE

This is an easy-to-make kite that can be made from a dustbin liner and two pieces of thin dowel.

Decoration can be added

PVC tape

Scale up to make from this plan

1.5 x length of kite

The vents can be varied a certain amount

A BALSAWOOD AEROPLANE

The balsawood aeroplane shown is made to withstand crashes. The front and rear wings are held on with elastic bands which 'give' in a crash. The elastic bands also allow adjustments to be made. The model can easily be taken to pieces for storage.

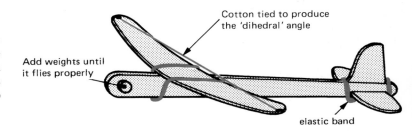

Cotton tied to produce the 'dihedral' angle

Add weights until it flies properly

elastic band

HOVERCRAFT 'ROUND THE POLE'

This model travels quite fast. (See also page 98 for help.)

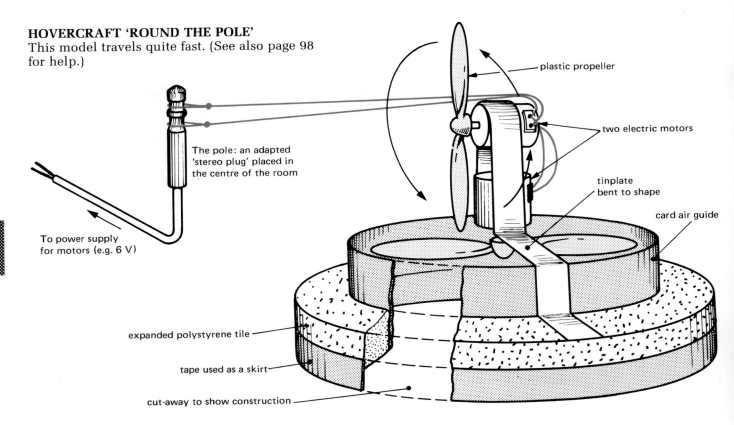

The pole: an adapted 'stereo plug' placed in the centre of the room

To power supply for motors (e.g. 6 V)

plastic propeller

two electric motors

tinplate bent to shape

card air guide

expanded polystyrene tile

tape used as a skirt

cut-away to show construction

MUSICAL PROJECTS

Compare sizes and tuning with schools musical instruments.

Banjo

Rectangular hole cut out for the wood beam

plastic container (e.g. old margarine tubs)

Tightening screw idea

hole

Tubular bells

cord

hard metal tubes (e.g. steel)

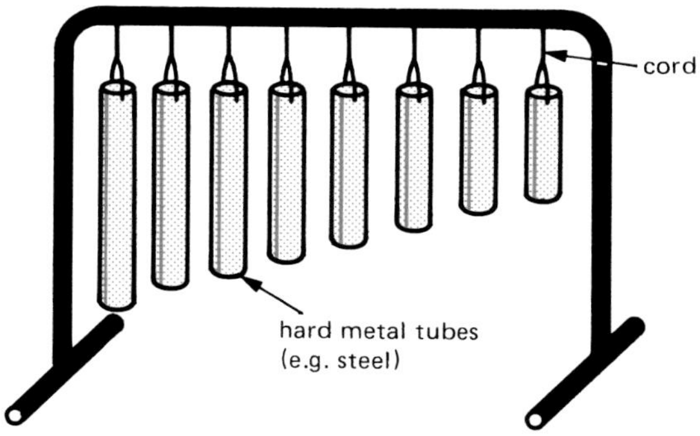

Chime bar

(More than one needed to play a tune)

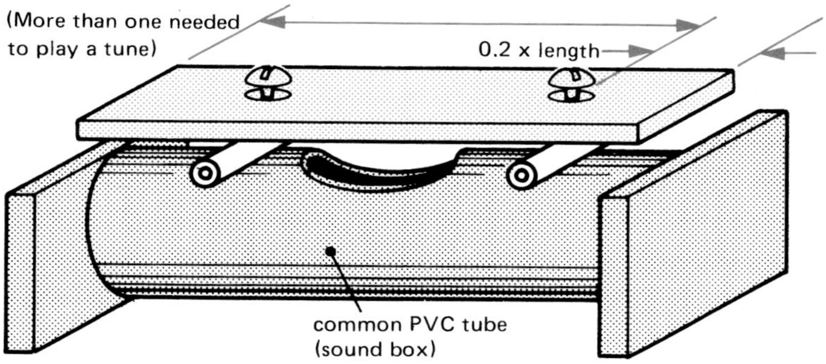

0.2 × length

common PVC tube (sound box)

Xylophone

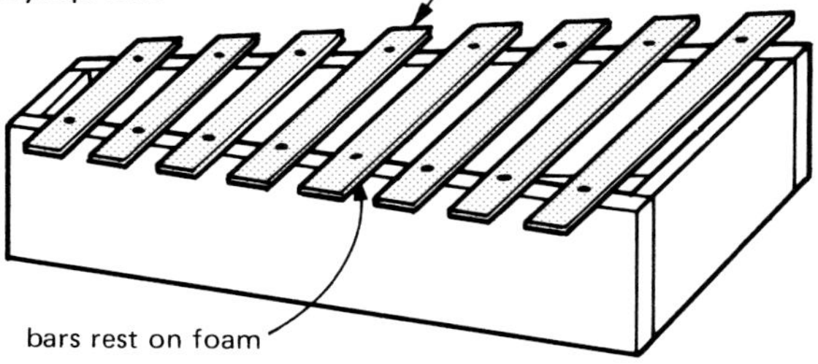

hard metal (e.g. steel)

bars rest on foam

HARMONOGRAPH

This makes random patterns on paper. Two ideas are shown. Also see page 81 for a photograph.
Note Make parts adjustable where possible.

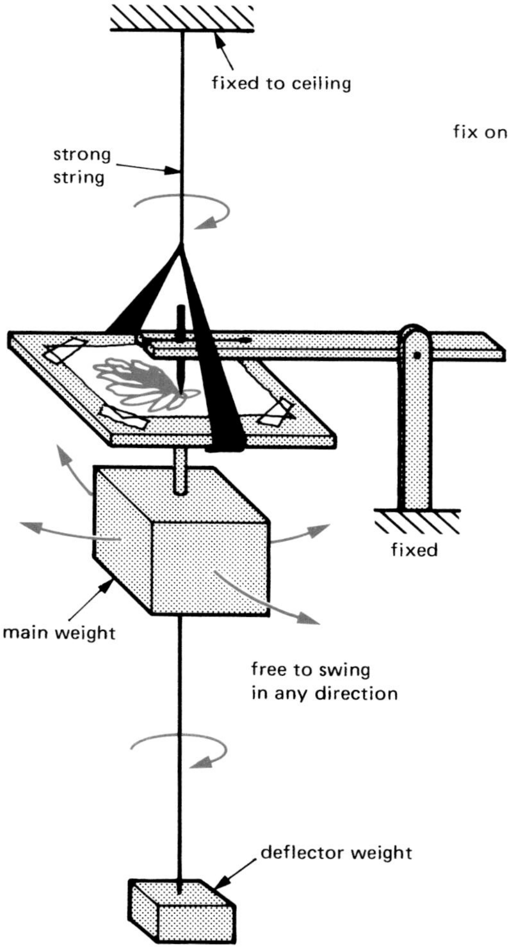

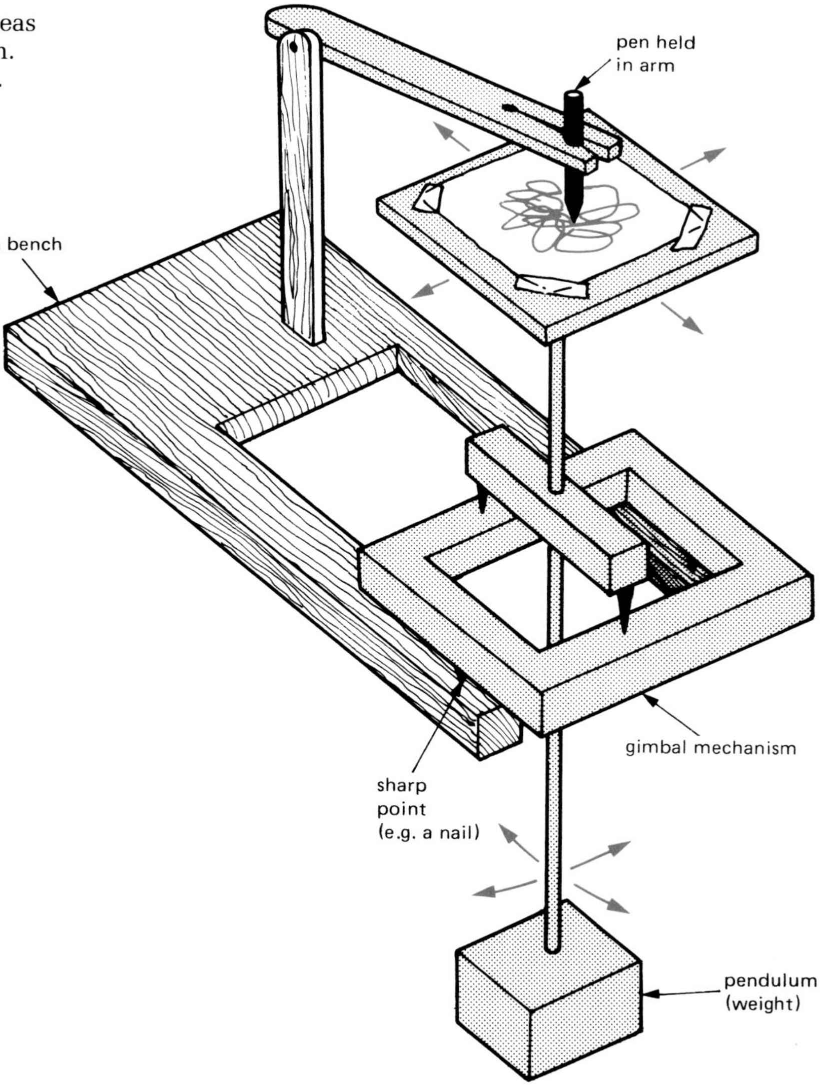

fixed to ceiling

strong string

main weight

free to swing in any direction

fixed

deflector weight

fix on a bench

pen held in arm

gimbal mechanism

sharp point (e.g. a nail)

pendulum (weight)

Other popular projects

TRANSPORT IDEAS

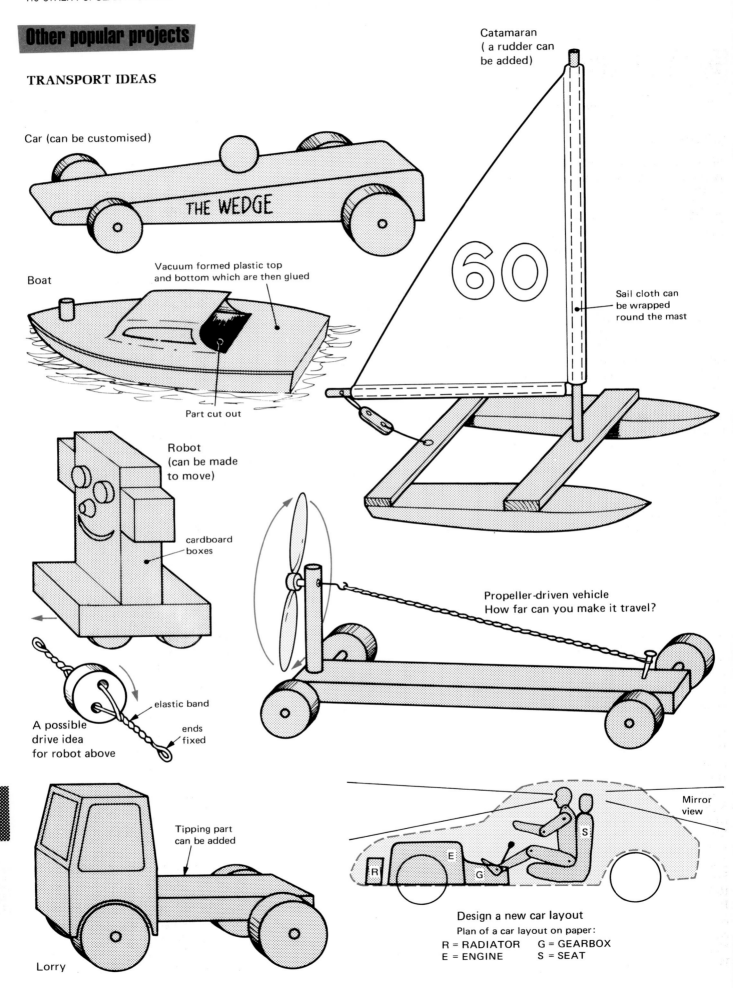

Car (can be customised)

THE WEDGE

Boat

Vacuum formed plastic top and bottom which are then glued

Part cut out

Catamaran
(a rudder can
be added)

60

Sail cloth can
be wrapped
round the mast

Robot
(can be made
to move)

cardboard
boxes

A possible
drive idea
for robot above

elastic band

ends
fixed

Propeller-driven vehicle
How far can you make it travel?

Tipping part
can be added

Lorry

Mirror
view

Design a new car layout
Plan of a car layout on paper:
R = RADIATOR   G = GEARBOX
E = ENGINE   S = SEAT

R E G S

APPENDIX

PROJECT IDEAS

The items are listed alphabetically. They include simple and difficult project ideas. The more difficult ones could be made by a class or a group of pupils.

MAINLY CRAFT

3D noughts and crosses
A theme based on nature
Action Man-type toy
Artificial hand
Bubble machine for disco
Car or bike anti-theft device
Cards (for an occasion-greetings)
Chair ergonomics
Clamp
Clip – decorated
Clock
Compass (directional)
Compass (for drawing)
Container – nuts, ash, fruit
Container – pens, cassettes, cards
Cutting board – bread, cheese etc.
Desk tidy
Dice or spinning top
Educational aids
Elastic band bounce game
Enamelling – brooches, initials etc.
Executive toys
Exerciser
Flying 'pull' bird
Fun hook
Game in a container
Games – draughts, Os and Xs etc.
Gyroscope

Hardness tester
Inclinometer
Jewellery – pendants, rings, bracelets
Jigsaw
Joint tester
'Jumping jack' pull toy
Key fob
Kinetic art
Laminated wood salad servers
Making use of recycled cans etc.
Marble roller coaster
Materials testers
Mobile
Models of futuristic houses etc
Modern lighting
Nameplate
Notepad holder
Pad saw holder
Pattern maker on paper
Pecking woodpecker toy
Pen holder
People counter/recorder
Percussion instruments
Photograph display or holder
Picnic bench
Pivoted toy
Plant pot holder

Play equipment
Polystyrene (expanded) model town
Pop-up cards
Pottery
Puzzles – jigsaw, interlocking
Rack – cassettes, books etc.
Resin casting
Sculpture – abstract – human etc.
Security system
Signs
Something that would be useful to the disabled
Sports aids
Stand for something, e.g. mike
Sundial
Survey of people's habits
T-square for homework
Tiles
Tools – hammer, hacksaw, screwdriver
Toys – tipping lorry, cars, puppets
Trysquare
Using a given part, design a ___?___
Vehicles
Wire shapes soldered, e.g. a human shape
Wire strippers

MAINLY TECHNOLOGICAL

General

A person sensor/counter
Air-powered vehicle
Automatic food dispenser
Automatic plant feeder
Baby alarm
Bike security device
Distance measuring, e.g. map roller
Doorbell for a deaf person
Electric powered bike
Hero's fountain
Hero's slot machine
Liquid level indicator
Mist propagator for plants
Model fork-lift truck
Model garage door opener
People counter
Plastics moulding machines
Polythene sheet sealer
Rainfall recorder
Reaction timer
Slot machine
Strength tester
Vehicle up a slope
Wake a deaf person

Water level indicator
Weather station
Weighing machine
Wind direction indicator

Electrics, Electronics and Computers

Advertisement display with lights
Ammeter
Amplifier
Camping light
Communication system
Computer aided design
Computer control, of vehicle etc.
Continuity tester
Disco effects
Doorbell
Electronic organ
Fire or cold alarm
Fuse tester
Hot-wire cutter for expanded polystyrene
Intercom
Joystick – control of vehicle
Metal detector
Metronome

Moisture detector
Musical device or instrument
Personal slide viewer
Piped light sign
Powered vehicle
Radio
Rain alarm
Reaction timer
Remote on and off controller
Steady hand game
Tape recorder control devices
Teaching machine
Timing device, e.g. for photography
Train set controller
White line follower
Windspeed indicator

Hydraulics and pneumatics

Boat hull shape testing
Hero's fountain
Linear air track
Model – crane, forklift, arm etc.
Punching or stamping machine
Tensile testing
Using syringes as cylinders

MAINLY TECHNOLOGICAL (continued)

Aerodynamics

Aerial photography – from a kite
Aeroplane – round the pole
Air track
Drag tester
Hot air balloon
Hovercraft
Kites
Land yacht
Parachute
Round the pole hovercraft
Storing wind energy
Wind speed measurement

Energy

Wind-up boat (elastic)
Engine tester (for power)
House heating/lighting etc.
Human energy tester/exerciser

Insulation
Model house
Projectile
Rubber band powered vehicle
Solar panel
Steam engine

Mechanisms

Catapult
Clock, e.g. water clock
Crankshaft, then add fun things
Engraver copier (pantograph idea)
Harmonograph
Map reader (distance)
Model vehicles
Model of a man riding bike
Music operated by cams and levers
Nodding toys, using cam or crank
Pantograph

Pedal car
Proportional dividers
Vehicle to climb up a steep slope
Walking robot
Weighing machines

Structures

Air supported
Bridges
Car layout in a monoque shell
Geodesic domes
Joint tester
Kites
Polaroid stress analysis
Ski lift towers
Spaceframe structure (no joints)
Strain gauges
Towers
Workbench

GRAPHICAL COMMUNICATION

2D drawings from 3D
3D drawings from 2D
Car badge
Customised car
Design illustration
Enlarging and reducing
Ergonome model – then use it
Ergonomic line drawings
Flow chart of people or work
Geometric patterns

Graphs and charts
House number
Ideograms
Loci
Logograms
Modular shapes
Name drawn in 3D
Optical illusions
Packaging, development of
Packaging for effect

Patio layout
Record cover
Safety poster
School plan
Sundial
Symbols
Symbols and conventions
Tile design
Vectors
Workshop layout and organisation

SET WORK — GENERAL

The work below is intended mainly for the odd lesson when ready-made CDT lessons are required.

1 TOOLS

Draw all the tools A to X shown here, starting with the ones you are most familiar with, adding

(a) The tool's **name**;

(b) a few words describing what use the tools are put to. You will need to refer to the section **Shaping and Forming Materials** (pages 54 ff.) for help.

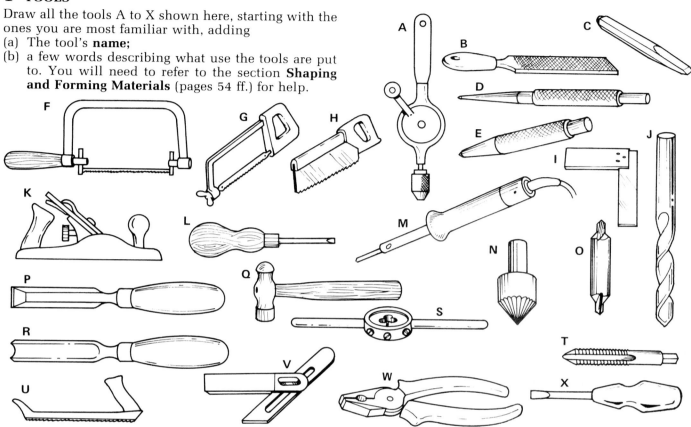

2 THE PLAN OF A ROOM

Draw a **room plan** based on a floor plan. Use the **planometric method**. Either (a) copy the drawing given; or (b) work from your own plan.

The stages are: (i) draw the plan on **grid paper to scale**, (ii) project **walls** up at 45 degrees; (iii) project **furniture** etc., (iv) complete by adding **details**.

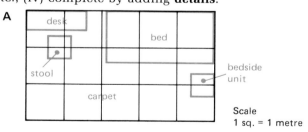

Scale
1 sq. = 1 metre

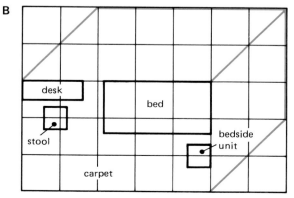

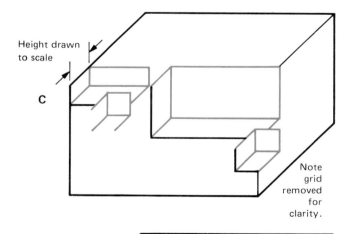

Height drawn
to scale

Note
grid
removed
for
clarity.

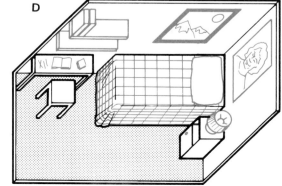

3 DESIGNING A LOGO

A **logo** is required for a firm for use on **envelopes** and for the side of the firm's **vehicles** (you choose the type of firm).

(a) **Sketch** out a few IDEAS for your firm's logo; then
(b) **draw** them on an **envelope** and **lorry** like the example shown.

Do not make the logo too complex.

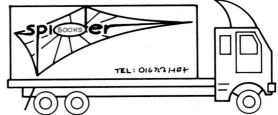

4 DRAWING YOUR NAME IN PERSPECTIVE

(a) Draw your name.
(b) Add the **vanishing point**.
(c) Draw lines from all the **corners** (some lines are shown).
(d) Complete and decorate the name (like the example).

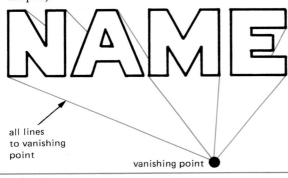

all lines to vanishing point

vanishing point

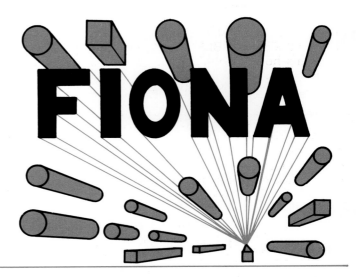

5 ROOM DRAWING
(using single point perspective)

1. Draw the **far wall**.
2. Add the **horizon** at **eye level**.
3. Select a **VP** (vanishing point).
4. Draw lines from the VP through the corners of the walls.
5. Add details.

General rules (see guide below)

(a) The uprights must be vertical.
(b) Horizontal lines (going into the distance) all go to the VP.
(c) Carefully estimate the depth of objects.

The example below was drawn by a 12-year-old.

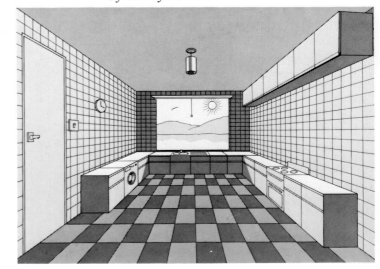

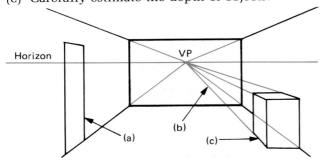

Horizon   VP

(a)   (b)   (c)

6 CAR LAYOUT

Design the layout of:
(a) a **sports car** with wheels 50 mm apart, or
(b) an **estate car** with wheels 70 mm apart
using the **outline drawings of parts**
provided below for a 1000 cc car
(scale 1 : 40).

Use thin white paper (or tracing paper) to
copy parts needed. See **Human Factors** on
page 118 for help on tracing human shapes.

Human shape

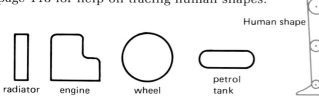

radiator   engine   wheel   petrol
tank

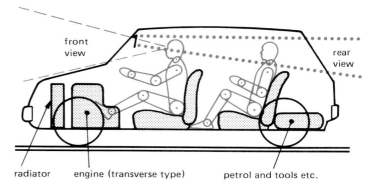

A family hatchback, Scale 1:40

front
view

rear
view

radiator   engine (transverse type)   petrol and tools etc.

7 ANIMATED ANIMAL OR FIGURE

(a) List six animals, figures, characters, cartoon
characters and androids etc. that could be made
into an interesting toy or ornament. At least one
part must move. (The head moves on the turtle
shown.)
(b) Draw out the BEST IDEA.
(c) DEVELOP THE BEST IDEA, explaining with diagrams how it could be made, which part/s move
and how.
(d) Colour either (b) or (c) above.

8 PACKAGE DESIGN

Design the outside of a package suitable for: a small toy,
a game, pens or glue. The finished container should
look professional; crayons etc. can be used. A possible
DEVELOPMENT layout is given below.

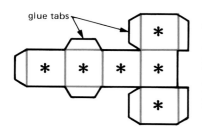

glue tabs

To make a cube using
A4 paper, the parts
marked * are all 70 mm
by 70 mm square.
Folds are marked in
red.

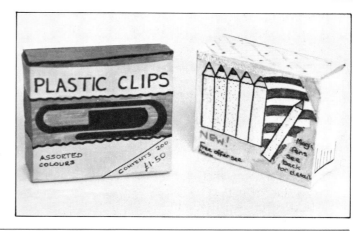

9 DESIGN – OWN CHOICE

Using the DESIGN PROCESS, design something that
you would like to make in the workshop, given the
chance, and are capable of making. If you cannot think
of anything to design, look at **Project Ideas**, pages 111–
12 for help.

(a) **State** what you want to make.
(b) INVESTIGATION – what it must do or be capable
of, in order to work. See the DESIGN PROCESS for
more help.
(c) **Sketch** at least three IDEAS.
(d) DEVELOP THE BEST IDEA, indicating:
  • the main sizes,
  • how each part could be made,
  • what joints could be used,
  • surface finish required etc.
(e) Make a WORKING DRAWING (if time).

10 DESIGN A FOLDER COVER

Design a **cover** for your **design folder** using the guide
below to help you.

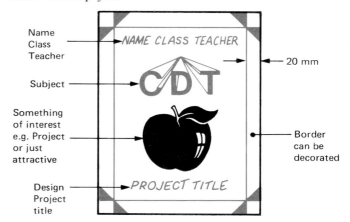

Name
Class
Teacher

NAME CLASS TEACHER

20 mm

Subject

CDT

Something
of interest
e.g. Project
or just
attractive

Border
can be
decorated

Design
Project
title

PROJECT TITLE

SET WORK — FINISHING OF MATERIALS

A summary of the most common ways of finishing (a) wood, (b) metal, and (c) plastics is given on this page (for more information see **Obtaining a Good Surface Finish** on page 65. The exercises here will help you remember the common finishing methods used.

Exercises

1 Copy **A. Wood Finishing.**
2 Copy **B. Metal Finishing.**
3 Copy **C. Plastic Finishing.**
4 Copy **Wood, Metal** and **Plastics Finishing.**

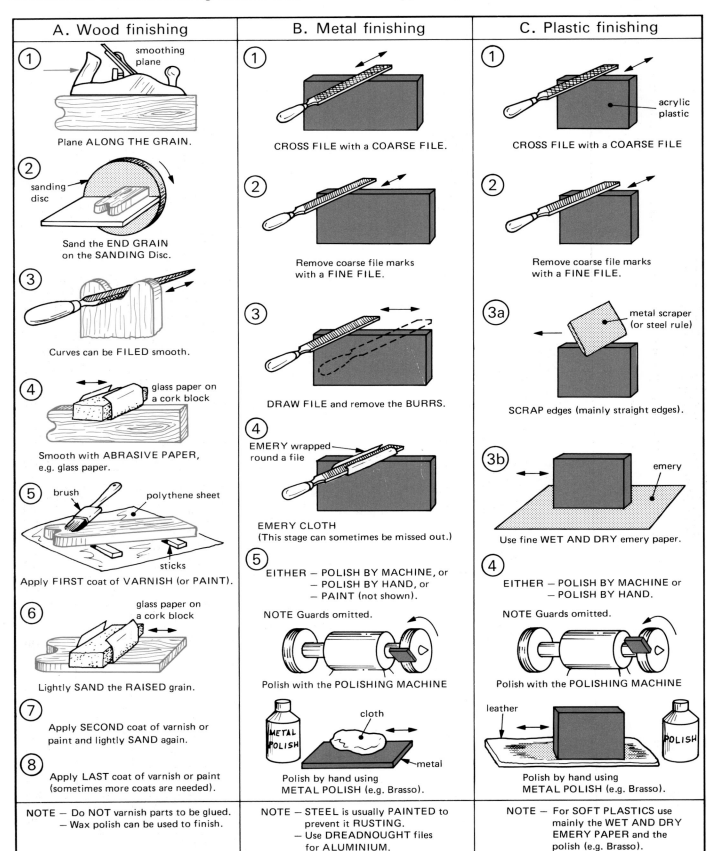

A. Wood finishing

① smoothing plane
Plane ALONG THE GRAIN.

② sanding disc
Sand the END GRAIN on the SANDING Disc.

③ Curves can be FILED smooth.

④ glass paper on a cork block
Smooth with ABRASIVE PAPER, e.g. glass paper.

⑤ brush   polythene sheet   sticks
Apply FIRST coat of VARNISH (or PAINT).

⑥ glass paper on a cork block
Lightly SAND the RAISED grain.

⑦ Apply SECOND coat of varnish or paint and lightly SAND again.

⑧ Apply LAST coat of varnish or paint (sometimes more coats are needed).

NOTE — Do NOT varnish parts to be glued.
— Wax polish can be used to finish.

B. Metal finishing

① CROSS FILE with a COARSE FILE.

② Remove coarse file marks with a FINE FILE.

③ DRAW FILE and remove the BURRS.

④ EMERY wrapped round a file
EMERY CLOTH
(This stage can sometimes be missed out.)

⑤ EITHER — POLISH BY MACHINE, or
— POLISH BY HAND, or
— PAINT (not shown).
NOTE Guards omitted.
Polish with the POLISHING MACHINE

cloth
METAL POLISH   metal
Polish by hand using METAL POLISH (e.g. Brasso).

NOTE — STEEL is usually PAINTED to prevent it RUSTING.
— Use DREADNOUGHT files for ALUMINIUM.

C. Plastic finishing

① acrylic plastic
CROSS FILE with a COARSE FILE

② Remove coarse file marks with a FINE FILE.

③a metal scraper (or steel rule)
SCRAP edges (mainly straight edges).

③b emery
Use fine WET AND DRY emery paper.

④ EITHER — POLISH BY MACHINE or
— POLISH BY HAND.
NOTE Guards omitted.
Polish with the POLISHING MACHINE

leather   POLISH
Polish by hand using METAL POLISH (e.g. Brasso).

NOTE — For SOFT PLASTICS use mainly the WET AND DRY EMERY PAPER and the polish (e.g. Brasso).

MATERIALS SELECTION CHART

USING THE CHART
This chart will help you to select the most appropriate material for a particular job. It can be used in two main ways:
1. Select a material and then check that it has the properties that you require.
2. Look at the properties first, then decide which material would be the best.

Question
What material would you choose if the following properties were required?
Tough, easy to work, flame resistant and reasonably light.

	HARDEST MATERIALS (HARDEST ●●●)	STRONG MATERIALS (TENSILE STRENGTH) (STRONGEST ●●●)	TOUGH MATERIALS (TOUGHEST ●●●)	CORROSION RESISTANCE (BEST ●●●)	WEIGHT (HEAVIEST ●●●)	EASY TO WORK (EASIEST TO WORK ●●●)	WILL IT BURN? YES/NO	MELTING OR SOFTENING TEMPERATURE (APPROX) (DEGREES CELSIUS)	COMMENTS
WOOD									
SOFTWOOD (e.g. pine)	●	●	●	●	●	●●●	Y	–	Yellowy brown. Weak across the grain. Needs protection if used outside.
HARDWOOD (e.g. oak, mahogany)	●●	●●	●●	●●	●	●●	Y	–	Creamy to a dark brown. More expensive than softwoods.
MANMADE BOARDS (e.g. plywood)	●	●	●●●	●	●	●●●	Y	–	Supplied in large sheets. Strong in both directions.
METALS									
MILD STEEL	●●	●●●	●●●	●	●●●	●●●	N	1500	Silvery grey. A very common metal. Rusts unless protected.
HIGH CARBON STEEL	●●●	●●●	●	●	●●●	●●	N	1400	Silvery grey. Used for making tools. Can be heat treated.
CAST IRON	●●	●●	●	●●	●●●	●●	N	1200	Silvery grey. Hard and brittle. Not usually used in schools.
STAINLESS STEEL	●●●	●●●	●●	●●●	●●●	●	N	1500	Shiny chrome look. Expensive. Hard to cut. Can come mirror polished.
ALUMINIUM	●	●	●●	●●	●	●●●	N	660	Silvery white. A light metal that cannot be soldered easily.
COPPER	●	●●	●●	●●	●●●	●●●	N	1050	Reddish-brown. Tarnishes. Expensive. Easily soldered and hammered into shape.
BRASS	●●	●●	●●	●●●	●●●	●●●	N	1000	Yellow brown. Expensive. Machines and solders easily.
PLASTICS									
ACRYLIC SHEET (e.g. perspex)	●●	●	●	●●●	●●	●●	Y	160	All colours and transparent. Polishes easily. Brittle if too thin.
PVC (polyvinyl chloride)	●	●●	●●	●●●	●●	●●●	Y	80	Various colours. Reasonably cheap. Can be supplied rigid or flexible.
POLYSTYRENE SHEET	●	●●	●●	●●●	●●	●●●	Y	100	Various colours. Glues and shapes very easily. Vacuum forms easily.
EXPANDED POLYSTYRENE	●	●	●	●●●	●	●●●	Y	95	White. Very light weight and easy to cut with a hot wire cutter.
NYLON	●	●●	●●●	●●●	●●	●●	Y	200	White or black. A tough plastic not easily glued. Machines quite easily.
POLYTHENE	●	●	●●●	●●●	●●	●●	Y	85	Clear. Difficult to glue but can be welded easily with a roller welder.
CAST POLYESTER RESIN	●●	●●	●	●●●	●●	●	N	–	**For embedding objects or used with glass fibre. Cannot be softened once set.**
OTHER									
PLASTER OF PARIS	●	●		●●	●●	●●●	N	–	Mixed with water and left to set. Rather brittle. Porous.
POTTERY	●●	●●		●●●	●●	●●	N	–	Clay needs to be 'fired'. Brittle. Hygienic washable surface once glazed.
CONCRETE	●●	●		●●●	●●	●●	N	–	Cheap. Strong in compression, but weak in tension.

HUMAN FACTORS (ERGONOMICS)

This page on **human factors** shows how to draw and make human scale models.

MAKING A CARD OR PLASTIC SHEET MODEL
- Copy **each** part of the body **separately**.
- Cut out each part very carefully. Label each part.
- Make 'pin joints' using a drawing pin.
- Assemble the model using drawing pins or bent wire.

DRAWING A HUMAN SCALE MODEL
- Trace the 'trunk' of the body.
- Select and draw round the next part, pivoting on the joint until you get the leg in the required position.
- Repeat for the other joints.

The **head**, **finger** and **hands** drawings can be traced and included in your design work as required.

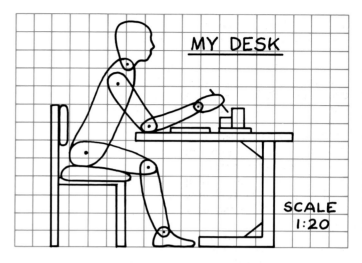

Scale 1:20   Each square represents 100 mm.

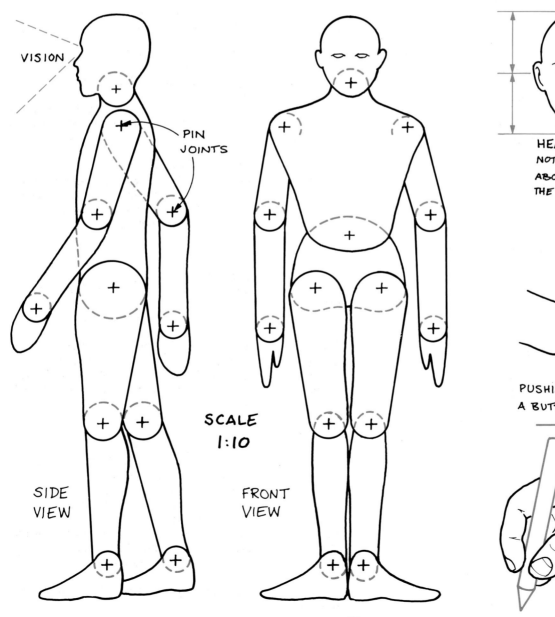

VISION

PIN JOINTS

SCALE 1:10

SIDE VIEW

FRONT VIEW

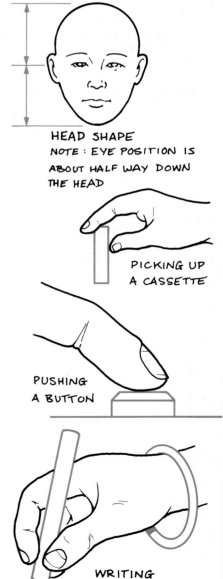

HEAD SHAPE

NOTE: EYE POSITION IS ABOUT HALF WAY DOWN THE HEAD

PICKING UP A CASSETTE

PUSHING A BUTTON

WRITING

The list of equipment below could form the basis for other workshops. It is based on a small multipurpose middle school workshop.

The equipment a school needs will depend on various factors such as: the school's timetable, the rooms used, how CDT is taught, the priorities set by the CDT adviser, the CDT teacher(s) and the headmaster etc.

MAINLY MACHINES
Circular saw – in a separate room
Pillar drilling machine
Machine vice – for drilling machine
Buffing (or polishing) machine
Vacuum former – hand operated
Disc sander
Brazing hearth – tongs, fire bricks etc.
Strip heater – C. R. Clark & Co.
Hegner saw. Pupils can safely use this.
Anvil, or something to hammer on
Guillotine – metal cutting – Gabro
Band saw – Coronet Tool Co.
Expanded polystyrene hot wire cutter – C. R. Clark & Co.
Small lathe, e.g. Emco Lathe + **various lathe tools:**
Grinder, with rough and smooth wheels
Woodwork lathe
Engraver (electrically operated)
Big benches with vices
Bench without vices – good for marking out large work
Teacher's bench, for demonstrations etc.
Jig saw – portable
Electric drill – portable
Electric sander – portable

HAND TOOLS
Oddleg calipers
Various cold chisels – large, small
Various screwdrivers – Pozidriv and flat types
Spanner set – 6 mm to 20 mm
Adjustable spanner – 10 in
Various metal saws – hacksaws, Abrafile
Engineering squares
Scribers
Centre and pin punches
Outside caliper, inside caliper, spring dividers
Centre finder
Pad saw – hacksaw blade type
Hammers – ball pein, Warrington, planishing, claw.
Mallets – types: egg head, cylindrical, nylon head, copper, rawhide
Hand drills – small and large (two speed)
Set of drills (1 mm – 13 mm+)
Starret hole saws – various sizes (for making wheels etc.)
Set of needlefiles
Tap and die set
Stanley plane – small 6 in
Bull nose plane
Coping saws
Tin snips – medium, large and curved
Pair of 'mole' grips
Spirit level
Leather hole punch – adjustable type

Vernier calipers
Drill gauge (0.5 mm – 10.5 mm)
Flat bits for wood (8 mm – 30 mm)
Letter and **number punch sets**
Surface gauge
Woodwork drill set, Jennings type
Countersink bits
Steel rules (300 mm)
Pliers – combination, round nose, flat nose pliers
Stanley knives
Wire brush
Rip/cross-cut saws
File cards
Set of mitre cramps
Rasps – medium, large
Beaten metalwork tools: dollies, sand bags, stakes
Brace, No. 66 – 10 in
Try square – large
Spoke shave
Surform files – standard, flat, round
Gouges – small, medium and large
Bradawls
G-cramps – ranging from small to large
Sash cramps (or new quick type)
Files – flat, round, half round, and dreadnought
Sets of Tools for Each Bench
  Planes; try squares; tenon saws; marking knives; mallets; hammers; marking gauges; chisels 6 mm, 9 mm; 12 mm steel rules

ELECTRICAL AND ELECTRONICS
Soldering irons – large and small
Electrical wire strippers
Electronics kits
Geared down electric motors + various bits and pieces (motors, bulbs etc. for projects)

COMPUTER
Computer – suitable for control work
Control interface – to control motors (with relays)
Buggy – school made or bought
Software – for CAD and control work etc.

ART AND GRAPHICAL COMMUNICATION
Rulers (for drawing)
Art brushes – large and small
Scissors – larger than the standard
Circle compasses
T squares
Paint pallettes
Drawing boards

OTHER
Acid bath and brass tongs for acid
Technical kits: Meccano or Technical LEGO® kits
Workmate bench – Black and Decker
Flammable materials storage cupboard
Safety things, e.g. aprons, goggles, masks etc.
Cabinets for nuts & bolts etc.
Use of overhead projector
Use of video recorder
Work storage
Display area and cabinet
Painting area
Large sink

Note Pottery, photography and enamelling equipment not included.

SAMPLE DESIGN SHEETS

Designs look good if they are presented in an organised and attractive way.

1 SMALL DESIGN SHEETS

When introducing design work with simple design problems, **two** sheets of folded normal A4 paper with the **printed information** on, can be used. When folded together they form an attractive booklet with a cover.

2 A4 DESIGN SHEETS

The four preprinted A4 design sheets shown can be used for all the other design work. Plain sheets can be added if required. Polythene folders (thick polythene bags) can be used to keep all your design sheets in. They allow the current design work to be seen without removing from the folder.

Other paper that may be needed

Tracing paper, isometric paper, square or grid paper (10 mm by 10 mm), plain and coloured card, A3 paper for larger designs.

COMPLETE
FOLDER
MADE
FROM TWO
A4 SHEETS

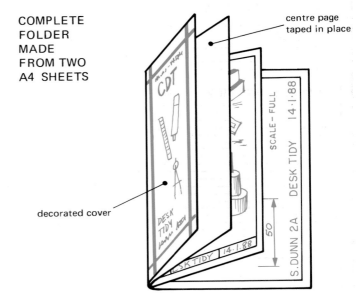

centre page taped in place

decorated cover

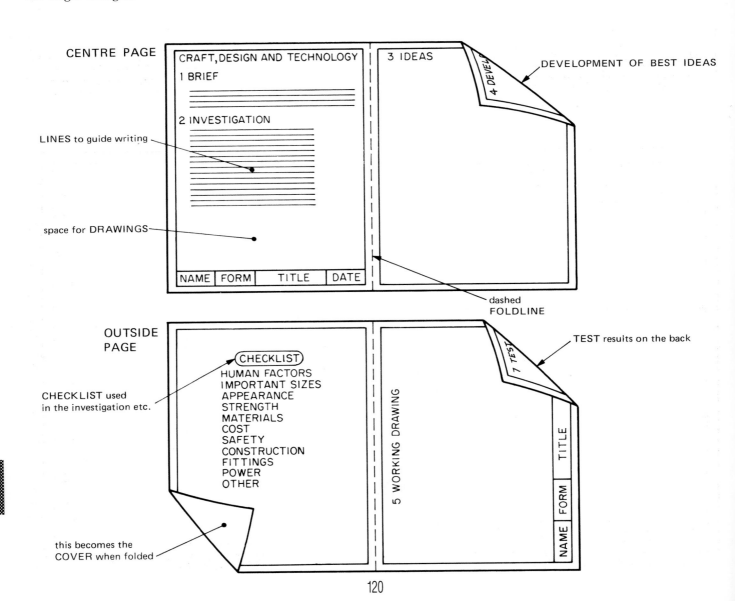

CENTRE PAGE

CRAFT, DESIGN AND TECHNOLOGY

1 BRIEF

2 INVESTIGATION

LINES to guide writing

space for DRAWINGS

NAME | FORM | TITLE | DATE

3 IDEAS

4 DEVELOPMENT

DEVELOPMENT OF BEST IDEAS

dashed FOLDLINE

OUTSIDE PAGE

CHECKLIST used in the investigation etc.

CHECKLIST
HUMAN FACTORS
IMPORTANT SIZES
APPEARANCE
STRENGTH
MATERIALS
COST
SAFETY
CONSTRUCTION
FITTINGS
POWER
OTHER

this becomes the COVER when folded

5 WORKING DRAWING

7 TEST

TEST results on the back

NAME | FORM | TITLE

Preprinted A4 design sheets for general use.

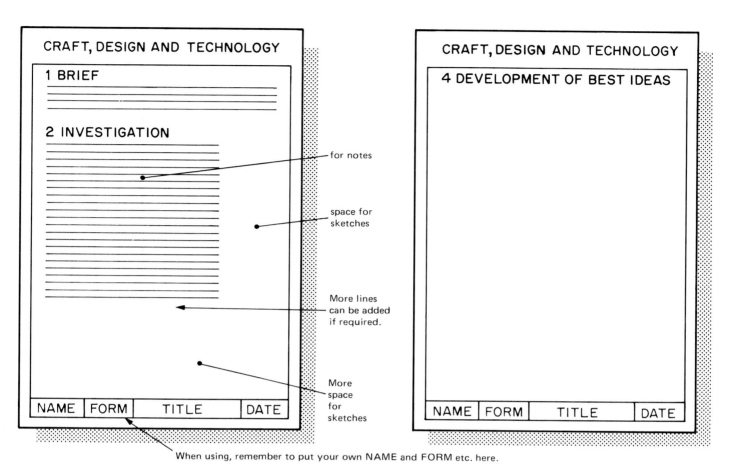

CRAFT, DESIGN AND TECHNOLOGY

1 BRIEF

2 INVESTIGATION

for notes

space for
sketches

More lines
can be added
if required.

More
space
for
sketches

NAME	FORM	TITLE	DATE

CRAFT, DESIGN AND TECHNOLOGY

4 DEVELOPMENT OF BEST IDEAS

NAME	FORM	TITLE	DATE

When using, remember to put your own NAME and FORM etc. here.

CRAFT, DESIGN AND TECHNOLOGY

3 IDEAS

Marks to help
divide up the
paper if
required.

Lines
added
by pupils
if wanted.

NAME	FORM	TITLE	DATE

5 WORKING DRAWING

SCALE | DATE

TITLE

NAME | FORM

REFERENCE SECTION

MAINLY FOR TEACHER USE

The National Centre for School Technology (NCST),
Trent Polytechnic,
Burton Street,
Nottingham NG1 4BU.

They can provide the following:
— The **NCST Magazine** *School Technology*

— The **Schools Council** *Modular Courses in Technology*
(They can be bought separately.)
Each course consists of:
1 A Teachers' Guide
2 A Pupils Book
3 A Workbook
The Module titles are:
Materials
Mechanisms
Structures
Energy
Electronics
Problem solving
Pneumatics
Instrumentation

— *Control Technology:*
Teachers' Book
Pupil Assignments
Follow-up Sheets

Craft, Design and Technology Yearbook and Directory **(Incorporating** *Craft Buyers' Guide***)**
This can be obtained from the Educational Institute of Design, Craft and Technology.

British Standards Institute Education Section,
2 Park Street,
London W1A 2BS.
— for British Standards publications

Technology Teaching Systems Ltd
Penmore House,
Hasland Road,
Hasland,
Chesterfield S41 0SJ.

For **Artstraws:**
Big Box Limited,
7 Newman Lane,
The Industrial Estate,
Alton, Hants, GU34 2QR.

For **Plastics:**
Trylon Limited,
Thrift Street,
Wollaston, Northants NN9 7QJ.
Resins and sheet plastics.

Economatics (Education) Limited,
Epic House,
9 Orgreave Road,
Dorehouse Industrial Estate,
Handsworth, Sheffield S13 9LQ.
They can supply LEGO® Technical kits, Meccano kits, Fischertechnik kits, the BBC Buggy and other technical equipment.

Maplin Electronic Supplies,
PO Box 3,
Rayleigh, Essex SS6 2BR.
Comprehensive catalogue.

RS Components Limited,
PO Box 99,
Corby, Northants NN17 9RS.
They supply electronic components. (Formerly known as Radiospares.)

For Metals and other hardware:
Heward and Dean Limited,
Schools Equipment Division,
90–94 West Green Road,
Tottenham,
London N15 4SR.
Free catalogue.

Note Your local DIY Superstore will stock double glazing plastic and PVC piping as well as wood etc.

BOOKS

Design and Craft
by A. Yarwood and S. Dunn
(Hodder and Stoughton)
For the Design Process.

Working with Materials
by Peter Stokes
(Nelson)
For more ideas.

Design Presentation
by David Beasley
(Heinemann Educational Books)

Introductory Design Problems
by K. Balkham and R. Mills
(Heinemann Educational Books)

Design Council
28 Haymarket, London SW1Y 4SU.
They publish various things: a useful and informative magazine is called *Designing*, a termly paper for students and teachers.

INDEX

123